Grade **3**

Scott Foresman

Fresh Reads

for Differentiated Test Practice

PEARSON
Scott Foresman

Editorial Offices: Glenview, Illinois • Parsippany, New Jersey • New York, New York
Sales Offices: Needham, Massachusetts • Duluth, Georgia • Glenview, Illinois
Coppell, Texas • Sacramento, California • Mesa, Arizona

ISBN: 0-328-16979-X

3 4 5 6 7 8 9 10 V004 14 13 12 11 10 09 08 07 06

Contents

Unit 1 Dollars and Sense

WEEK 1 Boom Town 1

WEEK 2 What About Me? 7

WEEK 3 Alexander, Who Used to Be Rich Last Sunday 13

WEEK 4 If You Made a Million 19

WEEK 5 My Rows and Piles of Coins 25

Unit 2 Smart Solutions

WEEK 1 Penguin Chick 31

WEEK 2 A Day's Work 37

WEEK 3 Prudy's Problem and How She Solved It 43

WEEK 4 Tops and Bottoms 49

WEEK 5 William's House 55

Unit 3 People and Nature

WEEK 1 The Gardener 61

WEEK 2 Pushing Up the Sky 67

WEEK 3 Night Letters 73

WEEK 4 A Symphony of Whales 79

WEEK 5 Volcanoes: Nature's Incredible Fireworks 85

Unit 4 One-of-a-Kind

WEEK 1 Wings **91**

WEEK 2 Hottest, Coldest, Highest, Deepest **97**

WEEK 3 Rocks in His Head **103**

WEEK 4 America's Champion Swimmer: Gertrude Ederle **109**

WEEK 5 Fly, Eagle, Fly! **115**

Unit 5 Cultures

WEEK 1 Suki's Kimono **121**

WEEK 2 How My Family Lives in America **127**

WEEK 3 Good-Bye, 382 Shin Dang Dong **133**

WEEK 4 Jalapeño Bagels **139**

WEEK 5 Me and Uncle Romie **145**

Unit 6 Freedom

WEEK 1 The Story of the Statue of Liberty **151**

WEEK 2 Happy Birthday Mr. Kang **157**

WEEK 3 Talking Walls: Art for the People **163**

WEEK 4 Two Bad Ants **169**

WEEK 5 Elena's Serenade **175**

© Pearson Education 3

Read the selection. Then answer the questions that follow.

Lucky Lucy

Lucy Mouse was excited. Today a new mouse was coming to class.

"Meet our new student, Ted Mouse," said Mr. Toad. "Let's make him feel welcome."

No one said a word. They were all staring because Ted had no tail!

At lunch, no one invited Ted to join them. Lucy felt sorry for Ted, but she was going to sit with her friends. Then she slipped and dropped all her food. No one said a word. They all just stared at her.

Only Ted walked over to Lucy. He said, "Don't worry. I'll help you."

Ted helped Lucy get more food. Then Ted and Lucy ate lunch together.

Turn the page.

Answer the questions below.

1 You know this story is a fantasy because the animals
- ○ stare.
- ○ eat.
- ○ walk.
- ○ talk.

2 Ted Mouse probably helped Lucy because he is
- ○ scared.
- ○ angry.
- ○ kind.
- ○ famous.

3 How is this fantasy *most* like a realistic story?
- ○ Two mice talk to each other.
- ○ Two students help each other.
- ○ The new student is a mouse.
- ○ The teacher is a toad.

4 What is the first clue that this story is a fantasy?

_____

_____

_____

_____

_____

_____

_____

_____

_____

_____

_____

© Pearson Education 3

Read the selection. Then answer the questions that follow.

Sanya's Science Report

Sanya was tired of looking at her screen and turned to look out the window. It was raining on Planet Octor. Sanya had to write a report for science class about a planet she had never visited.

Sanya's mom came into the room. "Why aren't you reading your teaching screen?" she asked.

"Oh, I have been. I've decided to write about Earth," Sanya said. "Why don't we go there? I can't think of a better way to learn about a planet."

Mom agreed, so they jumped into their spaceship and headed for Earth. Sanya looked out the window as they traveled. She recognized Norbeed, a red planet she and her family had visited on vacation. It still had a red halo around it.

Sanya knew from her teaching screen that Earth was different from Octor and Norbeed. Earth was a planet of blue water and green land. After three days, the blue and green planet came into view. Just as the spaceship was coming into landing orbit, Sanya heard a loud noise.

"Don't worry," Mom said. "That's just a signal from the Earth crew letting us know they're ready to pull us in."

Sanya smiled. She was eager to learn about Planet Earth.

Turn the page.

- -

Answer the questions below.

1 How was Sanya's mother like a real mom?
- ○ She wanted to help her daughter.
- ○ She knew how to fly a spaceship.
- ○ She visited Norbeed.
- ○ She lived on Octor.

2 What makes this story a fantasy?
- ○ It is about people making a long trip.
- ○ It gives facts about space travel.
- ○ It asks a question and gives more than one answer.
- ○ It is about something that could not happen.

3 How did Sanya feel at the end of the story?
- ○ proud
- ○ eager
- ○ worried
- ○ afraid

4 Which event in this story tells you it is a fantasy?
- ○ A girl had to write a science report.
- ○ A girl traveled to another planet.
- ○ A girl learned about another planet.
- ○ A family took a vacation.

5 What is the first clue that this story is a fantasy?

_____

_____

_____

_____

_____

_____

_____

© Pearson Education 3

Read the selection. Then answer the questions that follow.

The Fire Stealer

Once upon a time, there was no fire on the Earth, and animals everywhere were freezing. They could see the fire in the sun but could not get even a tiny coal from fierce Firekeeper, the sun's guardian. One day the animals were so cold they decided to steal some fire.

Brave Crow said, "I will fly to the sun and steal a coal. Firekeeper will not miss such a tiny piece."

But Firekeeper noticed him and was so furious that he burned the feathers off of Crow's head as punishment.

Then wiley Possum said, "Maybe I can steal some fire and hide it in my tail. Firekeeper will not notice a small coal hidden in my bushy tail."

But Possum could not fool Firekeeper, and angry Firekeeper burned the fur off Possum's tail as punishment.

Finally, tiny Water Spider said, "I will get so wet that the sun cannot burn me, and I will spin thread to make a little bowl on my back where I can carry the small piece of fire I will steal."

Water Spider was so small she could easily slip by Firekeeper. When the animals saw her carrying back the fire, they all cheered.

Bear said, "You are the smallest in our animal family, yet you gave us this precious gift of fire."

© Pearson Education 3

Turn the page.

Answer the questions below.

1 Based on Water Spider's actions, you can say that she was
- ○ small and afraid.
- ○ smart and brave.
- ○ big and strong.
- ○ sad and lonely.

2 You can tell this story is a fantasy because
- ○ there are no people in the story.
- ○ a problem is solved.
- ○ animals talk.
- ○ it takes place in the past.

3 How was Water Spider like a real person?
- ○ The sun could not burn her.
- ○ She was so small she could hardly be seen.
- ○ She talked with her animal friends.
- ○ She made a plan to do something.

4 How do you know that Firekeeper is not a real person?

_____

_____

_____

_____

5 What part of this story could really happen?

_____

_____

_____

_____

_____

Read the selection. Then answer the questions that follow.

First Place

Gene woke up sick. The music contest was on Monday. Gene was scared.

"I can't do it," Gene said to his parents.

"First you need to practice. I will help you," Gene's dad said. They practiced the piano together every day.

Then Gene and his dad went to the contest. Gene heard the other students play. They played very well. "I don't have a chance," Gene thought to himself.

Later it was Gene's turn. He looked at his dad and felt better. Gene played without any mistakes. He could not believe it when he heard his name called as the first-place winner.

Finally, Gene wasn't sick anymore.

Turn the page.

Answer the questions below.

1 The author probably wrote "First Place" to
○ tell a story about a boy who wins a contest.
○ persuade people to enter a music contest.
○ warn people to be patient.
○ teach people about music.

2 What was the *last* thing that happened in this story?
○ Gene and his dad practiced piano.
○ Gene heard his name called.
○ Gene wasn't sick anymore.
○ It was Gene's turn to play.

3 What did Gene *probably* do just after he played the piano in the contest?
○ took another turn
○ called his dad
○ went back to his seat
○ started to cry

4 What do you think Gene and his dad most likely did after the contest?

_____

_____

_____

_____

_____

_____

_____

_____

_____

_____

_____

Read the selection. Then answer the questions that follow.

The Backyard Party

Angie and Gina wanted to have a party because school was almost over for the summer. They wanted to invite all their friends, but their houses were too small for so many people. Gina thought that her big backyard would be perfect for the party, so she asked her mom if she could have the party there. Gina's mom agreed, so the girls began to make plans for the best party ever.

First, Angie and Gina made a list of their friends. Then they made fancy invitations that told the time and place of the party. Next, Angie began writing names on the cards, while Gina made a list of food to buy. Because the weather was warm, Gina wanted to have ice cream for dessert.

"What games should we play?" Angie asked.

"Let's play the ring-toss game that we played last summer," Gina said.

Just then Gina's mom came into the room. "What's the date of the party?" she asked.

Gina and Angie looked at each other and laughed. They had been so busy making plans for the party that they'd forgotten to pick a day for it!

Turn the page.

Answer the questions below.

1 What do you think Gina and Angie will do next?
- ○ give the invitations to their friends
- ○ pick a day for the party
- ○ give Gina's mom a list of food to buy
- ○ practice the ring-toss game

2 What clue words tell you the sequence of events in the second paragraph?
- ○ made, began
- ○ first, then, next
- ○ told, because
- ○ time, place

3 The author probably wrote this story to
- ○ persuade the reader to have a party.
- ○ express a point of view.
- ○ entertain the reader.
- ○ give facts about summer.

4 Which of the following happened first?
- ○ Gina got permission to have the party.
- ○ Angie and Gina made invitations.
- ○ Gina's mom asked about the date of the party.
- ○ Gina and Angie made a list of friends to invite.

5 If you were planning a party, what would you do first, second, and third?

_____

_____

_____

_____

_____

_____

_____

Read the selection. Then answer the questions that follow.

Henry's New Bed

My cat Henry could sleep almost anywhere and anytime. Sometimes I found him

curled up in an armchair, or sleeping on a pile of clothes, or napping in my bed.

One day my mom told me that it was time for Henry to have a bed of his own.

"Carl, you should make a bed for Henry," Mom said. "I'll help you."

First, we looked for a basket in the basement and found an old laundry basket

that we didn't use anymore. Next, we needed something soft for Henry to sleep on.

I suggested my pillow, but Mom didn't think that was a good idea. She found some

old towels and put them in the basket. I wanted to show the bed to Henry right

away, but Mom said that we should put one of his favorite toys in the basket first. I

found Henry's toy mouse and put it in the basket.

"Now we need to find a place to put Henry's bed," Mom said.

We decided to put Henry's bed on the floor near my bed. When I showed Henry

his new bed, he jumped right in, turned around a few times, and then quickly fell

asleep. From then on, we found him in his own bed more often than in mine.

Turn the page.

Answer the questions below.

1 What happened right *after* Mom and Carl found the basket for Henry?

○ Henry jumped into the basket.

○ Carl found Henry's toy.

○ Carl found a place for the basket.

○ Mom found some towels.

2 The author probably wrote this story to

○ describe a funny cat.

○ explain how to make a cat bed.

○ persuade the reader to buy a cat.

○ frighten the reader.

3 Henry saw his new bed for the first time right *after* Mom and Carl

○ put the towels in the basket.

○ found a basket.

○ looked for a basket.

○ found a place for the bed.

4 Why was it important to put one of Henry's favorite toys in the basket *before* showing him his new bed?

_____

_____

_____

_____

_____

5 What are the clue words that tell you the sequence of events in this story?

_____

_____

_____

_____

_____

Read the selection. Then answer the questions that follow.

Makoto's Garden

Every day after school Makoto helped her grandmother in the garden. One day Makoto asked her grandmother if she could have a plant of her own.

Grandmother smiled and said, "First, get a pot and fill it with dirt from the shed."

Makoto came back with a pot filled with dirt. "What's next?" she asked.

Grandmother showed Makoto some packages of seeds.

"What do you want to grow?" she asked.

Makoto chose the tomato seeds. Then her grandmother showed her how to bury the seeds in the dirt and gently water them.

"Now the pot needs to get some sun," said Grandmother.

Turn the page.

Answer the questions below.

1 When did Makoto plant her seeds?
- ○ after she watered them
- ○ after she put the dirt in the pot
- ○ after she put the pot in the sun
- ○ before she got the dirt from the shed

2 How can you tell that Makoto liked gardening?
- ○ She liked tomatoes.
- ○ She knew how to plant seeds.
- ○ She asked for her own plant.
- ○ She played outside after school.

3 If the pot of seeds gets enough sun and water, what will happen *next*?
- ○ It will be time for school.
- ○ Grandmother will be angry at Makoto.
- ○ Tomato plants will start to grow.
- ○ Makoto will fill the pot with dirt.

4 What will Makoto and her grandmother *probably* do *next* with the pot?

_____

_____

_____

_____

_____

_____

_____

_____

_____

_____

_____

Read the selection. Then answer the questions that follow.

Hot Dog Wraps

Here is a treat for your whole family. You will need some help to make them.

You will need:
    butter
    4 slices of bread
    4 slices of cheese
    4 hot dogs

Spread butter on each slice of bread. Spread it on one side only. Then put the bread on a baking sheet with the butter side down. Put one slice of cheese on each slice of bread. Put one hot dog across each slice of cheese. Place the hot dog from one top corner to the opposite bottom corner of the bread.

Then ask a grown-up to help you turn on the oven to 375°.

Next, for each slice of bread, fold the two other corners over the hot dog. Push two toothpicks through the bread and into the hot dog to hold them together. This is what makes the wrap.

Ask for help putting the baking sheet into the oven. Bake for about 10 minutes. The bottoms of the bread should be a light brown. Ask for help again to take the baking sheet out of the oven. Use a spatula to put the hot dog wraps on plates.

Eat up!

Turn the page.

Answer the questions below.

1 What do you do right *after* you put the hot dog on the bread?
- ○ Wait for ten minutes.
- ○ Put the cheese on the bread.
- ○ Put butter on one side of the bread.
- ○ Get help turning on the oven.

2 What is happening while you are wrapping up the hot dogs?
- ○ The hot dogs are cooking.
- ○ The oven is heating.
- ○ The cheese is melting.
- ○ The bread is turning brown.

3 Why do you use a spatula to take the wraps off the baking sheet?
- ○ to keep the hot dogs from falling off
- ○ so that you will not burn your fingers
- ○ so that you will not need help
- ○ to make sure they are done on top

4 What would you do *before* you started making Hot Dog Wraps?
- ○ Turn on the oven to 375°.
- ○ Butter the bread and cook the hot dogs.
- ○ Make sure a grown-up was around to help.
- ○ Tell your family that dinner was ready.

5 Why must you butter the bread first?

_____

_____

_____

_____

_____

_____

_____

_____

Read the selection. Then answer the questions that follow.

Basketball Practice

Benny and Derrick walked to the gym together for basketball practice as they did every Saturday morning. There they found a note from Coach Saba taped to the door. The note said that the coach had been called away and that practice would begin one hour late.

Benny and Derrick did not want to walk all the way back home, so they walked to the bookstore instead. When they got there, the store was closed. They started walking back to the gym, but on the way they met Rafael. The three friends decided to walk to the park.

After walking through the park, the boys headed back toward the gym. On the way, they met Erica who was going to the library. The four friends walked to the library together.

When Benny and Derrick finally got back to the gym, Coach Saba was waiting for them.

"OK, we're going to warm up by running around the gym," he said.

"Oh, no," said Benny. "I feel as if I already ran around the gym at least twice."

And the two friends began to laugh.

Turn the page.

Answer the questions below.

1 What was the *first* thing Benny and Derrick did in this story?

○ found the note from Coach Saba

○ met Rafael

○ walked to the gym

○ went to the bookstore

2 What will Benny and Derrick *probably* do now?

○ run around the gym

○ say hello to Erica

○ wait for the coach to get there

○ walk home

3 Why did Benny feel as if he had already run around the gym?

○ He was upset that practice started late.

○ He had been to the library.

○ He had gotten up early.

○ He had been walking for an hour.

4 What *probably* would have happened if Benny and Derrick had met Erica before they met Rafael?

_____

_____

_____

_____

_____

5 Tell what Erica *most likely* did at the library. Use sequence words in your answer.

_____

_____

_____

_____

_____

_____

Read the selection. Then answer the questions that follow.

Pond Day

Shandra and her mom lived in a small underground hole near a pond. Pond Day was coming soon. Shandra planned to paint some smooth stones to give as gifts to her mouse friends.

"Let's paint one stone for each season," said Shandra's mom.

First they found some stones. Then they got some paint and brushes.

"For fall, I will paint leaves in bright fall colors," said Shandra.

They began painting, and as each stone was finished, they put it in the sun to dry. Shandra looked at the colorful stones.

"This will be the best holiday ever," thought Shandra.

Turn the page.

Answer the questions below.

1 What is the *first* thing that Shandra does in this story?
- ○ chooses a season to paint
- ○ decides what to make as gifts
- ○ gets some bright paint and brushes
- ○ dries some smooth stones

2 What tells you that Shandra is *not* a real person?
- ○ She lives with her mother.
- ○ She celebrates holidays.
- ○ She lives in an underground hole.
- ○ She lives near a pond.

3 Which of these could *not* happen?
- ○ a mouse painting stones
- ○ a mother helping a daughter
- ○ a friend giving gifts
- ○ a painted stone drying in the sun

4 What part of this story could really happen?

_____

_____

_____

_____

_____

_____

_____

_____

_____

_____

_____

Read the selection. Then answer the questions that follow.

The Rabbit Thief

Nolo was a clever but lazy rabbit. He did not want to work for his food like the other animals. One day Katutu, the elephant king, called the animals together to build a new village. All the animals worked except Nolo. Instead of working, Nolo hid near the kitchen until the cooks left. Then he ate all the beans they had cooked for dinner.

When Katutu returned and learned that all the beans were gone, he was very angry. But Mbo, the turtle, had a plan to catch the thief.

Mbo said, "Tell your cooks to hide me in the pot of beans."

The next day the cooks did as Mbo asked. Soon Nolo came to steal the beans, but just as Nolo began to eat, Mbo jumped up, bit his nose, and held on tight.

When the king and the other animals came home from the forest, they found Mbo hanging on to Nolo's nose. Mbo had caught the thief just as she had planned.

The king ordered that Nolo should not eat for three days, and Nolo never stole again.

© Pearson Education 3

Turn the page.

Answer the questions below.

1 You can tell this story is a fantasy because the animals
- ○ have unusual names.
- ○ work together.
- ○ plan to catch a thief.
- ○ live in a forest.

2 Which event in this story could really happen?
- ○ an elephant king building a village
- ○ a rabbit eating beans
- ○ a turtle asking to hide in a pot of beans
- ○ cooks listening to a turtle's plan

3 When did Katutu learn that the beans were gone?
- ○ after working all day
- ○ before leaving for work
- ○ after calling the animals together
- ○ after hearing Mbo's plan

4 In this story, which event could *not* really happen?
- ○ a village being built
- ○ a king asking for help
- ○ a rabbit not eating for three days
- ○ an animal cooking beans

5 How is this story like a realistic story?

_____

_____

_____

_____

_____

_____

_____

_____

Read the selection. Then answer the questions that follow.

Friends Helping Friends

A long time ago an ant was walking in a forest and growing thirsty. He went to the lake for a drink of water. Suddenly a strong wind blew the ant into the water.

"Help!" cried the ant. "I can't swim."

Nearby in the lake a duck was paddling about, and she heard the ant's cry for help. She swam as fast as she could to where the ant was struggling to stay above water. "Climb onto my beak," she said, "and I'll carry you to shore where you'll be safe." Then she lowered her beak to the level of the water so that the ant could climb onto it.

Safe on shore, the ant thanked the duck for saving his life. "You are very welcome," said the duck. "I was glad to be able to help."

Then, as the duck was swimming away, the ant noticed a hunter walking toward the lake, surely planning to shoot the duck. The ant hurried toward the hunter, climbed up his leg, and bit him hard, again and again. The hunter screamed out in pain and dropped his gun. Hearing the commotion, the duck saw the hunter and quickly flew away to safety.

Turn the page.

Answer the questions below.

1 What tells you that this story is a fantasy?
- ○ A duck swam to shore.
- ○ A hunter walked toward a lake.
- ○ An ant walked in a forest.
- ○ An ant talked to a duck.

2 Which of these happened *last*?
- ○ An ant helped a duck.
- ○ An ant was thirsty.
- ○ A duck helped an ant.
- ○ An ant saw a hunter.

3 Which of these could *not* really happen?
- ○ A hunter screamed.
- ○ An ant yelled for help.
- ○ A duck flew away.
- ○ An ant bit a person.

4 Write one thing that happens in this story that could really happen.

_____

_____

_____

_____

_____

5 What might the duck say to the ant the next time they see each other?

_____

_____

_____

_____

_____

Read the selection. Then answer the questions that follow.

The Clever Crow

Once upon a time a crow was flying home from school. He was tired and thirsty. He saw a glass on a table by the road and flew over to look inside. There was a little water at the bottom but he could not reach it. He tried to tip the glass over but it was too heavy. Then he picked up some stones and dropped them into the glass. As he dropped the stones, the water began to move to the top. Soon the crow could reach the water with his beak. The clever crow took a drink and flew away.

Turn the page.

Answer the questions below.

1 Where does this story take place?
- ◯ at school
- ◯ at home
- ◯ by a road
- ◯ near a pond

2 What tells you that this story is a fantasy?
- ◯ The crow was thirsty.
- ◯ The crow flew home.
- ◯ The crow could pick up stones.
- ◯ The crow went to school.

3 What word best describes the crow in this story?
- ◯ gentle
- ◯ foolish
- ◯ creative
- ◯ careless

4 What do the crow's actions tell you about his character?

_____

_____

_____

_____

_____

_____

_____

_____

_____

_____

_____

Read the selection. Then answer the questions that follow.

Chatty Charlie

Charlie Chipmunk loved to talk. When Charlie got to school in the morning, he told his friends about his pet cat. In the afternoon, Charlie told everyone about his favorite soccer team. Charlie also liked to answer Mr. Owl's questions even when Mr. Owl had asked other students to answer.

Charlie's teacher called Charlie's mom and dad. "Can you help me stop Charlie from talking so much?" he asked.

Mr. Chipmunk had an idea. He told Charlie, "Put this rubber band on your wrist. Then when you feel like talking, pull it instead."

The next day Charlie was surprised. It seemed as if he was pulling the rubber band all day! On the second day, Charlie didn't pull it as much. On the third day, Charlie hardly pulled the rubber band at all.

Now Charlie didn't do all the talking. When the teacher asked a question, Charlie let other students answer. Charlie listened to his friends' stories instead of always telling his own stories.

"You did it, and we're proud of you, Charlie," said his mom and dad. "You can take the rubber band off now."

"I think I'll keep it on to remind myself to be quiet. But not all the time," Charlie said and laughed.

Turn the page.

Answer the questions below.

1 What is one reason that Charlie talked too much?

○ He came from a family that talked a lot.

○ He did not realize he was talking so much.

○ He thought he knew more than everyone else.

○ He was nervous, and talking calmed him down.

2 Which of Mr. Owl's actions tells you that he cared about his students?

○ He called Charlie's parents.

○ He wanted Charlie to answer all his questions.

○ He took his students on field trips.

○ He told Charlie to stop talking.

3 What tells you that this story is a fantasy?

○ A teacher is annoyed with a student.

○ A student answers a teacher's questions.

○ Parents talk to their son.

○ Animals talk to each other.

4 Where does most of the story take place?

○ at a store

○ at the beach

○ at school

○ at a party

5 What did Charlie learn by wearing the rubber band?

_____

_____

_____

_____

_____

_____

_____

Read the selection. Then answer the questions that follow.

Libby's Dad

My dad repairs spaceships. He has a garage near my school where customers bring their vehicles to be fixed. Every day after school, I fly to my dad's shop and usually find him inside a ship. When I say hello, he pokes his head out, his face covered with grease and his hands full of wires.

"Hello, Libby. How was school?" he always asks.

Even though he's busy, he listens while I tell him about the events of my day.

People are constantly flying in and out of the shop. Dad always listens closely to what they tell him. From that, he estimates what needs to be done and how much it will cost them. Generally they smile and shake his hand.

Sometimes my dad finds things people have left behind in their spaceships. Once he found a wallet. He called the owner immediately, and needless to say, the man was quite relieved.

After the shop closes, my dad and I put all the tools back on their racks and use the Skyvac to clean up.

Yesterday, just as we had finished cleaning, a woman came to get her ship.

"I hope you grow up to be just like your dad," she whispered to me as she was getting ready to leave.

"I do too," I whispered to myself.

Turn the page.

Answer the questions below.

1 **What words best describe Libby's dad?**
- ○ careful about his appearance
- ○ trusted and admired
- ○ less than honest
- ○ too busy to listen

2 **Where did this story mostly take place?**
- ○ in a parking lot
- ○ at school
- ○ on the way home
- ○ in a garage

3 **What tells you that this story is a fantasy?**
- ○ people fly into the shop
- ○ a man fixes vehicles
- ○ a girl goes to school
- ○ people lose things

4 **What do the actions of Libby's dad tell you about him?**

_____

_____

_____

_____

5 **What can you tell about Libby from the way she describes her dad?**

_____

_____

_____

_____

_____

Read the selection. Then answer the questions that follow.

Dogs with Jobs

Dogs make good pets. Many dogs have special jobs too.

Dogs have a very good sense of smell. This means they can help find people who are lost.

Some dogs are trained to help people who can't see or hear well. For example, these dogs learn to point out a ringing telephone to people who can't hear. The dogs become good friends to the people they help.

Dogs also cheer up older people who may be lonely. People often feel happy when they can pet a dog.

Dogs work hard every day. They make life easier for many people.

Turn the page.

Answer the questions below.

1 **What is the main idea of this selection?**

○ Dogs make good pets and do many jobs.

○ People need dogs to help them every day.

○ Only dogs with good hearing and sight can be trained.

○ Dogs cheer up people who are older or lonely.

2 **What must happen *before* a dog can help someone answer the phone?**

○ The dog and the person have to be friends.

○ The dog needs a good sense of sight.

○ The person has to feed the dog.

○ The dog needs to be trained.

3 **What is the main idea of the second paragraph?**

○ A dog's sense of smell helps it to find missing people.

○ Dogs have a very good sense of sight.

○ Dogs are trained to find missing people.

○ When people get lost, a dog can find them.

4 **What would be another good title for this selection?**

_____

_____

_____

_____

_____

_____

_____

_____

_____

_____

_____

Read the selection. Then answer the questions that follow.

The Real Dr. Seuss

You have probably heard of Dr. Seuss. Have you heard of Theodor Seuss Geisel? Ted Geisel used the name Dr. Seuss when he wrote *The Cat in the Hat* and *Green Eggs and Ham*.

Ted Geisel did not start out as a children's author. At first, he wrote for adults. He also drew cartoons. On a trip in 1937, Ted Geisel wrote his first book as Dr. Seuss. He used the name Seuss because it was his middle name. He used the title of Dr. because his father wanted him to be a doctor.

In 1954, Ted read an article about problems children were having learning to read. The article said that children's books were boring. Ted's boss gave him a challenge. Could he write a book children would enjoy using only 250 words? Nine months later, Ted gave his boss *The Cat in the Hat*. The book used only 220 words. It was an instant success.

In 1960, Ted was given another challenge. Could he write a children's book using only 50 words? Yes, *Green Eggs and Ham* was the happy result.

When Ted Geisel died in 1991, he had written more than 44 books. More than 200 million copies had found their way into homes and hearts around the world.

Turn the page.

Answer the questions below.

1 **What is this selection *mostly* about?**

   ○ how Dr. Seuss wrote *Green Eggs and Ham*

   ○ why children have trouble reading

   ○ the man who wrote the Dr. Seuss books

   ○ why Dr. Seuss used so few words in his books

2 **Which of these would *not* be a supporting detail for this selection?**

   ○ Ted Geisel was born in Springfield, Massachusetts, in 1904.

   ○ Dr. Seuss also wrote *How the Grinch Stole Christmas*.

   ○ Dr. Seuss was not a great poet.

   ○ Dr. Seuss's books have been translated into more than 15 languages.

3 **When did Dr. Seuss have his *first* success?**

   ○ when he changed his name to Dr. Seuss

   ○ when he wrote *Green Eggs and Ham*

   ○ when he started writing for adults

   ○ when he wrote *The Cat in the Hat*

4 **What is the main idea of the first paragraph?**

   ○ Dr. Seuss read about children learning to read.

   ○ Dr. Seuss's real name was Theodor Seuss Geisel.

   ○ Theodor Geisel was a successful children's author.

   ○ Ted Geisel first wrote for adults, not children.

5 **Why do you think the author called this selection "The Real Dr. Seuss"?**

_____

_____

_____

_____

_____

_____

_____

Read the selection. Then answer the questions that follow.

Flying Dragons?

Have you ever seen a dragon fly? Maybe not, but if you are near a pond in the summer, you may see an insect called a dragonfly. Even though their name makes them sound fierce, dragonflies do not harm people. In fact, people are happy to see them because they eat other insects that people do not like.

These small, thin, winged insects have been around for more than 300 million years. They are born under the water, grow up in the mud, and live in the air for only one or two months.

Most people learn to identify dragonflies by their wings, which shimmer in colors such as green, purple, and blue. Their wings are stronger than they look, carrying the dragonflies at about sixty miles an hour. That's about as fast as a car on a highway.

Every year millions of dragonflies move from place to place, always settling near water. It is a stunning sight, but scientists still do not know why they do this.

If you are lucky enough to see these striking insects this summer, you can thank them for being such beautiful and helpful friends.

Turn the page.

Answer the questions below.

1 **What is the topic of this selection?**
- ○ insects
- ○ dragonflies
- ○ flying dragons
- ○ nature

2 **What is the main idea of this selection?**
- ○ Dragonflies are small, thin, winged insects.
- ○ Scientists do not know why dragonflies settle near water.
- ○ Dragonflies are helpful and beautiful insects.
- ○ Dragonflies have been around for 300 million years.

3 **When do dragonflies appear fully grown?**
- ○ after millions of years
- ○ after one or two months
- ○ after settling near water
- ○ after living in mud

4 **What are two supporting details from the first paragraph?**

_____

_____

_____

_____

_____

5 **What is the main idea of the third paragraph?**

_____

_____

_____

_____

_____

Read the selection. Then answer the questions that follow.

Jonah's Sled

When Jonah woke up, he saw that the ground was white with snow. He looked for his sled. Where could he have left it? He put on his boots. He could only find one glove. Also, his hat seemed to be missing. He kept his hands in his pockets, but his head felt cold as he walked down the street looking for his sled.

Finally, Jonah gave up and started to walk back home. Just then he saw his sister Sasha in front of the house.

"Thanks for letting me borrow your sled," said Sasha.

"No problem," said Jonah. "I'm just glad to know where it is."

Turn the page.

Answer the questions below.

1 What does this story tell you about Jonah?
- ○ He comes from a big family.
- ○ He likes to stay inside during the winter.
- ○ He is a little forgetful.
- ○ He gets angry easily.

2 What tells you that this is a realistic story?
- ○ It is about something that could happen.
- ○ It is about a brother and sister.
- ○ Jonah wakes up and goes sledding.
- ○ Jonah lost his boots.

3 Which detail helps you know what Jonah is like?
- ○ He saw that the ground was white.
- ○ He put on his boots.
- ○ His glove and hat are missing.
- ○ He saw his sister Sasha.

4 Would you lend your favorite toy to Jonah? Explain.

_____

_____

_____

_____

_____

_____

_____

_____

_____

_____

Read the selection. Then answer the questions that follow.

Saturday Morning

Marlene, Tremain, and Leticia spent the day together on Saturday. They met at the ancient oak tree near the royal castle. The three elves didn't have any definite plans yet, but it was early.

Marlene offered the idea, "Let's fly to the park."

Tremain stated that his wing was still sore from the games they played the week before. He had injured his left wing.

"We can walk to the park," Marlene suggested.

Leticia complained that her leg was still hurt from an accident the previous day. She had fallen off a branch and hit the ground before she could start flying.

Marlene exclaimed, "Let's play Name the Elf!" They did not need to fly or walk to play that game. But Tremain and Leticia complained that they already knew all the elves' names, so it would not be any fun.

Marlene pronounced, "We can watch the telescreen."

Leticia responded that there was nothing interesting to watch on Saturday morning.

"Then we can listen to music," Marlene shared.

Tremain did not want to do that.

"Well, what do you want to do?" Marlene inquired. She was beginning to wish she had stayed home. Tremain glanced at Leticia. Leticia looked at Marlene.

"I know," Leticia replied. "Let's perform a good deed."

© Pearson Education 3

Turn the page.

Answer the questions below.

1 **What does this story tell you about Marlene?**
- ○ She is one of the leaders of the elves.
- ○ She is not interested in many things.
- ○ She has a hard time keeping her temper.
- ○ She does not give up easily.

2 **How can you tell this story is a fantasy?**
- ○ Tremain and Leticia are not names of real people.
- ○ There are no such things as elves.
- ○ An oak tree would not be near a castle.
- ○ A wing could not be injured.

3 **How did Marlene *probably* feel at the end of the story?**
- ○ surprised that Leticia wanted to do something
- ○ sorry that her friends had been injured
- ○ happy that the elves had met near the castle
- ○ angry that Leticia had a good idea

4 **What do Tremain and Leticia's actions tell you about them?**
- ○ They are brother and sister.
- ○ They love to play games.
- ○ They are hard to please.
- ○ They are easily excited.

5 **Do you think Marlene will want to do what Leticia suggests? Explain.**

_____

_____

_____

_____

_____

_____

Read the selection. Then answer the questions that follow.

Corey's Lesson

Corey sat at his desk staring at his closed science textbook. "I don't care if I fail the stupid test," he muttered to himself. Just then Dan walked into the room.

"Dan, why do I need to know about the rain forest anyway?" Corey asked his older brother. Corey and Dan were friends as well as brothers. They shared many of the same interests. Corey especially liked to go bike riding with Dan because Dan knew all the best biking trails.

Dan thought about Corey's question. "You have to study about the rain forest so that you can learn how to protect it," he said.

"Why does it need to be protected?" Corey asked.

"In a lot of ways, it can't protect itself," Dan said. "And the animals and plants that live there are in danger of dying out completely. So, if they no longer exist, we can't learn from them or use them."

Corey was surprised because he didn't know that some animals were in danger of becoming extinct. Now he was more interested in learning about the rain forest.

"I'll make a deal with you," Dan said. "You study for an hour, and then I'll go bike riding with you. We'll go on that special trail I was telling you about."

"It's a deal," said Corey eagerly as he opened his book.

© Pearson Education 3

Turn the page.

Answer the questions below.

1 **What does this story tell you about Dan?**

　○ He is thoughtful and cares about his brother.

　○ He likes to go bike riding more than anything else.

　○ He is much older than Corey and thinks he knows best.

　○ He acts as if he knows more than he really does.

2 **What will Corey *probably* do for the next hour?**

　○ go for a bike ride

　○ study for his science test

　○ ask Dan about the rain forest

　○ take a test on the subject of the rain forest

3 **What tells you that this is a realistic story?**

　○ The characters act like real people.

　○ The rain forest does *not* really exist.

　○ Dan and Corey do not get along.

　○ Corey studies for his math test.

4 **How does Corey change during the story?**

_____

_____

_____

_____

_____

5 **What does Corey's change in attitude tell you about him?**

_____

_____

_____

_____

_____

Read the selection. Then answer the questions that follow.

Rania's Sign

Rania and her sister were helping to clean up the beach. There were lots of bottles and cans in the sand. Rania wanted to get her friends to help too. She decided to make a sign to tell her friends about it.

Clean Up the Beach!

When: Every Saturday morning, 8 A.M.
Where: All-City Beach

Be sure to bring boots and gloves.
Bring garbage bags if you can.

YOU Can Make a Difference!

Help make the beach
a safe place to play.

Rania knew that once her friends read the sign, they would want to help too.

Turn the page.

Answer the questions below.

1 **What is this passage mostly about?**

- ○ Rania's Saturday morning
- ○ Rania and her sister
- ○ Rania's effort to help
- ○ Rania going to the beach

2 **Where would Rania *probably* put her sign?**

- ○ at school
- ○ on a car
- ○ at the train station
- ○ on her front door

3 **What do Rania's actions tell you about her?**

- ○ She does not work well with others.
- ○ She likes to swim in the ocean.
- ○ She wants more than her share of things.
- ○ She does not think only of herself.

4 **Why does Rania think her friends will want to help too?**

_____

_____

_____

_____

_____

_____

_____

_____

_____

_____

Read the selection. Then answer the questions that follow.

Simon's Pets

My friend Simon is lucky. He has a saltwater fish tank with many kinds of fish. The salt water means that Simon can keep tropical fish, the colorful fish that live in the oceans.

Simon's three favorite fish are Annie, Red, and Polly. Annie is a clown fish. She is orange with white wavy stripes on each side. Annie is shy and likes to hide near the "live rocks" at the bottom of the tank. Simon says that the live rocks are like living filters that keep the water clean.

Red is a flame angel fish. He is bright red with black bands on each side. Whenever Simon comes near the tank, Red comes to the side because he thinks he will get something to eat.

I like Polly the most. She is orange with bright green squiggly lines all over her. Simon says that he can have only one of these fish in the tank at a time. Simon doesn't know why, but that's what his fish book says.

Simon and I like to spend time watching the fish and reading about how to take care of them. It's my favorite hobby too.

Turn the page.

Answer the questions below.

1 **What is this passage mostly about?**

○ fish that live in the ocean

○ how to care for a fish tank

○ Simon's fish tank

○ Simon's best friend

2 **What can you tell about Simon by the way he treats his pets?**

○ He likes to solve puzzles.

○ He is a good student.

○ He is greedy.

○ He is responsible.

3 **What is one thing Simon likes about tropical fish?**

○ their bright colors

○ the food they eat

○ the way they feel

○ the way they sound

4 **What do you think might happen if the tank had no "live rocks"?**

○ Some of the fish would become less colorful.

○ The water would lose some of its salt.

○ The fish would have no place to hide.

○ The water would become less healthful.

5 **What are three things Simon needs to know about his pets?**

_____

_____

_____

_____

_____

_____

_____

© Pearson Education 3

Read the selection. Then answer the questions that follow.

The Dog Ate My Homework

My dog Olive loves to eat paper. We've tried to stop her many times but she just keeps eating it. She seems to like my homework the best.

Once, I let Olive into my room before I put my homework away. She grabbed it and ran out the door as I chased after her. When she stopped, she glanced at me, wagged her tail, then quickly chewed up the paper before I could catch her. The next day, I had to tell my teacher that the dog ate my homework.

Now, whenever I do my homework, my mom states, "Sara, be sure to put your homework into your book bag as soon as it is finished."

Last night I let Olive into my room too soon, and of course, she grabbed my homework, ripped it up, and gobbled it down before I could save it. "What will I tell my teacher now?" I thought to myself.

The next morning when the teacher asked for my homework, I told him that I didn't have it.

"Your dog again?" he inquired with a skeptical tone in his voice.

"I can't blame Olive this time," I replied. "It was my fault for forgetting to put my things away."

I never again had to tell my teacher that the dog ate my homework.

Turn the page.

Answer the questions below.

1 What is this story mostly about?
- ○ a dog who ate Sara's homework
- ○ dogs that cause trouble
- ○ adventures of a girl and her dog
- ○ a girl who learned a lesson

2 What did Mom tell Sara to do when she finishes her homework?
- ○ Put it in her book bag.
- ○ Let Olive into her room.
- ○ Take Olive for a walk.
- ○ Talk to her teacher.

3 Why do you think Sara opened the door to her room too soon?
- ○ She does not like her room.
- ○ She is eager to play with Olive.
- ○ Her mom is calling to her.
- ○ She is tired of doing homework.

4 Do you think Sara got angry at Olive for eating her homework? Explain your answer.

_____

_____

_____

_____

_____

5 What do Sara's actions tell you about her?

_____

_____

_____

_____

_____

Read the selection. Then answer the questions that follow.

The Disappearing Pile of Leaves

It was a beautiful fall day. Dad and I were raking leaves into a big pile. My dog Penny was chasing leaves as they fell off the trees. Dad and I were cold, so we went into the house to make some hot chocolate. When we went back outside, the pile of leaves was gone! We started making another pile. Soon, Mom called us in for lunch. When we went back outside to finish our job, the pile was gone again!

Dad laughed and petted Penny. He said, "Before we start another pile, let's put Penny in the house."

The next pile of leaves did not disappear.

Turn the page.

Answer the questions below.

1 Why do you think the author wrote this story?
- ○ to explain how to rake leaves
- ○ to share information about dogs
- ○ to make the reader smile
- ○ to describe a beautiful fall day

2 Why did the pile of leaves disappear?
- ○ A fall breeze blew the pile away.
- ○ There never was a real pile of leaves.
- ○ The street cleaners picked up the leaves.
- ○ Penny played in the pile and scattered the leaves.

3 How does the author want you to feel about the job of raking leaves?
- ○ that it is fun
- ○ that it is a hard job
- ○ that it cannot be done
- ○ that it has to be done fast

4 How does the author tell you how Dad feels about Penny?

_____

_____

_____

_____

_____

_____

_____

_____

_____

_____

Read the selection. Then answer the questions that follow.

Eduardo's Sea Shells

Eduardo is a "sheller." That's the name for a person who picks up sea shells. He lives in Florida, so there are many beaches where he can look for shells that have washed up on the shore. All he needs is a pail and some shoes to protect his feet. He also reads books about shells so that he can learn their names.

Eduardo has many ideas about how to display his shells. He puts some shells around a picture frame. With his mother's help, he makes holes in some shells and puts them on a string. His mother thinks the shells look like jewels, and she likes to wear them around her neck. Eduardo gives some shells to his friends. They use them to make their fish tanks look more natural.

Eduardo's favorite idea for the shells is to fasten them to pieces of wood he finds on the beach. He hangs these pieces on the wall in his room. He likes to lie on his bed and look at them.

Eduardo knows that there are many more ideas for using shells, but he already has a good start.

Turn the page.

Answer the questions below.

1 **Why do you think the author wrote this story?**

○ to persuade the reader to collect sea shells

○ to inform the reader about different ways to use shells

○ to express feelings about sea shells and "shellers"

○ to describe the best way to look for sea shells

2 **What is this story mostly about?**

○ the ways Eduardo uses sea shells

○ sharing treasures with friends

○ finding and selling sea shells

○ making gifts for your mom

3 **Why did the author say that Eduardo only needs a pail and some shoes?**

○ to show that Eduardo was serious about sea shells

○ to show that Eduardo was not prepared to collect shells

○ to show that you should protect yourself on the beach

○ to show that collecting shells is not an expensive hobby

4 **Why do you think the author compares shells on a string to jewels?**

○ to make shells seem like art

○ to show that shells can be expensive

○ to show how beautiful shells can be

○ to explain that shells are easy to find

5 **Name two things that the author wants you to know about Eduardo.**

_____

_____

_____

_____

_____

_____

_____

Read the selection. Then answer the questions that follow.

Totem Poles

If you have studied about America long ago, you have probably read about totem poles. The first totem poles were made by Native Americans who lived near the Pacific Ocean.

The totem poles were tall poles made from redwood trees. A skilled artist carved people, animals, and make-believe creatures into the poles. Long ago, the Native Americans did not have a written language. The carvings on the poles were used to explain how each Native American tribe lived and what was important to them. The carvings also described the myths and legends of a particular tribe.

Originally, part of the procedure involved raising the totem pole. A hole was dug, and the pole was nested in it. Because the poles were large and heavy, the raising process required many people with ropes. During the raising ceremony, a speaker explained the details and stories behind the carvings. The people of the tribe listened to and remembered the stories so that the stories could be passed down.

Learning about totem poles helps you understand what was important to other people. It might also inspire you to think about what is important to you.

Turn the page.

Answer the questions below.

1 Why do you think the author wrote this selection?
- ○ to persuade students to study American history
- ○ to express feelings about the history of Native Americans
- ○ to describe the Native Americans who lived by the ocean
- ○ to explain a Native American custom

2 What is the author's purpose in the last paragraph?
- ○ to interest the reader to learn more
- ○ to inform the reader about the purpose of totem poles
- ○ to encourage the reader to admire Native American culture
- ○ to persuade the reader to protect historic totem poles

3 Which of these items has a purpose similar to that of a totem pole?
- ○ a telephone pole
- ○ a loudspeaker
- ○ a book
- ○ a map

4 What is the author's purpose in the third paragraph?

_____

_____

_____

_____

_____

5 Why does the author tell you about the importance of totem poles?

_____

_____

_____

_____

_____

Read the selection. Then answer the questions that follow.

A New Girl in Class

Keiko is a new girl in school. She moved here from Japan. She is learning to speak English.

Our class is learning about people from other countries. Our teacher told us to choose a country and find pictures of food or clothing that show how the people live.

One day, Keiko surprised the class. She came to school wearing a beautiful dress. It was bright blue and soft. It didn't look like any of my dresses! Then she shared some food from her country. I was a little nervous about tasting it, but after everyone ate some, I did too. It was delicious.

That was our most interesting class and the most fun!

© Pearson Education 3

Turn the page.

Answer the questions below.

1 What did this story tell you about Keiko?
- ○ She did not like surprises.
- ○ She liked American food.
- ○ She was excited to learn English.
- ○ She was proud of her country.

2 Why did Keiko wear her Japanese dress to class?
- ○ The class was studying people from other countries.
- ○ It was Keiko's birthday, and she wanted to dress up.
- ○ Keiko wanted to be special.
- ○ The other students asked Keiko to wear it.

3 Why was Keiko's classmate nervous about eating Japanese food?
- ○ There was not enough to share.
- ○ It was different and might taste bad.
- ○ She knew it wasn't good for her.
- ○ It looked familiar but tasted different.

4 How do you think Keiko felt after class?

_____

_____

_____

_____

_____

_____

_____

_____

_____

_____

_____

Read the selection. Then answer the questions that follow.

It's for the Birds

Sometimes, I just do not understand Julie. She loves to watch birds! She has four bird feeders in her yard, and the birds are always flapping around making a lot of clatter. Then, Julie and her friends stand around watching and listening to the birds. They won't move or talk because the birds will fly away. What fun is that?

Julie even bought a machine that makes bird sounds. Now it seems as if I hear bird noises coming from inside her house too.

Sometimes her friends from the bird club come to her house to plan new bird-watching trips or to look at pictures of birds from earlier trips. Last year, the club went to a beach in Texas to watch birds for three days. When I asked Julie if she went swimming while she was at the beach, she said that she didn't have time. I just don't understand how she could be at a beach and not go swimming.

Last spring Julie made houses for the birds. I saw the eggs and the baby birds after they were born. Now there are even more birds!

There are many things I don't understand, and Julie's interest in birds is one of them.

Turn the page.

Answer the questions below.

1 **What conclusion can you draw about Julie's friends?**

○ They are girls.

○ They like to go swimming.

○ They are bird watchers like Julie.

○ They are scientists and teachers.

2 **Who do you think wrote this selection?**

○ a neighbor

○ a friend in another city

○ a teacher

○ Julie herself

3 **What did you learn about Julie from this story?**

○ She loves cats.

○ She is bored.

○ She is lonely.

○ She is patient.

4 **When Julie said she did not have time to go swimming, she meant that**

○ none of her friends wanted to go swimming.

○ she wanted to spend her time watching birds.

○ the beach was too far.

○ she spent all her time lying on the beach.

5 **Why do you think someone would like to watch birds?**

_____

_____

_____

_____

_____

_____

_____

Read the selection. Then answer the questions that follow.

The Spider Catcher

Walter woke up feeling excited because his dad was taking him into the field. His dad was a zoology professor, and today they were hunting for spiders. Most people are afraid of spiders, but not Walter. He has been helping his dad find insects, frogs, and all kinds of creatures since he was a little boy.

Walter put on tall boots and his hat. He grabbed the spider catcher, which looks like a long handle with a brush at one end and a lever on the other end. The spider catcher allows Walter to catch spiders without harming them, and it makes releasing them easy too.

When Walter and his dad got to the field, they walked slowly and looked carefully in the tall grass and under rocks. Dad said that spiders live almost everywhere on Earth, except in very cold places like mountaintops. Spiders even live in holes on beaches.

Walter noticed a web and stopped. He saw a large spider, took out the catcher, and was about to capture the spider when it jumped onto Walter's shirt.

"Be very still," Dad said. "It won't hurt you. It's a jumping spider."

Dad got the spider into a glass dish and closed the cover.

"It looks as if I did not need to buy a spider catcher after all," said Dad as he began to sketch the spider in his notebook.

Turn the page.

Answer the questions below.

1 How do you know that Dad will not keep the spider?

○ The spider catcher makes releasing the spiders easy.

○ Spiders live almost everywhere on Earth.

○ Walter's dad was a zoology professor.

○ Walter's dad put the spider into a glass dish.

2 Why do you think Walter put on tall boots?

○ Tall boots were the most comfortable.

○ It was raining and the field was muddy.

○ Walter wanted to protect himself.

○ Those were the only boots Walter had.

3 Where did most of this story take place?

○ in the mountains

○ in a field

○ near a river

○ in a swamp

4 How did Dad know that the jumping spider wouldn't hurt Walter?

_____

_____

_____

_____

5 Why does the spider catcher have a long handle?

_____

_____

_____

_____

© Pearson Education 3

Read the selection. Then answer the questions that follow.

He Had a Dream

Dr. Martin Luther King, Jr., had a dream. He grew up when the laws of the United States said that black people and white people were not equal. He knew this was wrong, so he began to work to change the laws.

In 1955, a black woman named Rosa Parks would not give her seat on a city bus to a white man. She went to jail. Dr. King heard about it. He got people to stop riding buses until the law was changed.

In 1960, Dr. King heard about a restaurant where white people would not serve black people at the lunch counter. Dr. King joined the people sitting at the counter, and he was put in jail. In the end, Dr. King's efforts and hard work changed many laws. His dream still lives on today.

Turn the page.

Answer the questions below.

1 **What was Dr. Martin Luther King, Jr.'s dream?**

○ He wanted to help white people.

○ People would not break the laws and go to jail.

○ Black people could ride buses.

○ All people would be treated equally someday.

2 **Why did Rosa Parks go to jail?**

○ She broke the law.

○ She asked Dr. King to help her.

○ She told people to stop riding buses.

○ She changed the law.

3 **Why did black people stop riding buses?**

○ The law said they could do it.

○ They wanted a law to be changed.

○ They did not want to go to jail.

○ They could not afford to pay the fare.

4 **Why was Dr. King put in jail for sitting at a lunch counter?**

_____

_____

_____

_____

_____

_____

_____

_____

_____

_____

Read the selection. Then answer the questions that follow.

A Stormy Day

Gordon watched the summer sky grow darker while his mom and dad prepared

for the thunderstorm that was coming. Gordon knew that thunderstorms could be

fierce and dangerous. His neighbors had lost part of their roof and some big trees

the year before. Gordon's neighbors were lucky because no one got hurt, not even

their dog, Bruno.

Gordon heard the wind getting louder and saw the trees bending. Then, he heard

thunder in the distance. Soon, a flash of lightning lit up the sky. He was not very

worried, though, because his family was well prepared. Gordon had made sure all

the water bottles were full in case there was no clean water to drink after the storm.

His dad carried enough blankets and pillows to the shelter to keep their family

warm and comfortable. His mom brought flashlights, a portable radio, and extra

batteries. Just then, they heard rain on the roof.

"Ready to go down?" asked Dad.

When Gordon's family got into their shelter, they turned on the radio. They heard

that the storm was not getting stronger and that there was no danger after all. Even

though Gordon was safe in the shelter, he was glad to hear the radio announcement.

"Well, we got ready for nothing," Gordon said.

"No," Dad said. "It's always better to be safe than sorry."

Turn the page.

Answer the questions below.

1 **Why did Gordon say that his family got ready for nothing?**
- ○ because their neighbors didn't need help
- ○ because the storm was not dangerous
- ○ because they had enough water bottles
- ○ because Gordon's family liked storms

2 **Why did they need flashlights, a portable radio, and extra batteries?**
- ○ because the storm could cause flooding
- ○ to help walk downstairs
- ○ in case they lost electric power
- ○ in case the storm took their roof off

3 **What part of the storm had done most damage to the neighbors?**
- ○ the rain
- ○ the hail
- ○ the thunder
- ○ the wind

4 **Why did Gordon's dad take blankets and pillows to the shelter?**
- ○ to protect them from the rain
- ○ because they had to cover the windows
- ○ in case they had to spend the night in the shelter
- ○ because the neighbors told them it was a good idea

5 **What did it mean when Gordon heard the wind getting louder?**

_____

_____

_____

_____

_____

_____

_____

Read the selection. Then answer the questions that follow.

A Ball of Rock

You are probably not surprised when you see Earth's moon, but you might be surprised by some facts about it.

We know that the moon is about 4.5 billion years old because that is the age of the rocks astronauts brought back from the moon. Most experts believe Earth is about the same age.

Did you know that if you speak on the moon, no one would hear you? On Earth, you can hear sounds because sound needs air to travel through. Since there is no air on the moon, no sounds can be heard. Therefore, when astronauts walked on the moon, no one could their footsteps.

Also, because there is no air, the sky is always black on the moon. Light, like sound, needs air to travel through. It is the light traveling through air that creates different colors, such as the blue of the sky.

There is no wind on the moon either. Footprints left on the moon by astronauts will be there for millions of years because there is no wind or air to disturb the footprints.

Scientists once thought that the moon had no water and that nothing could live there. Recently they found frozen water, so scientists now believe it is possible that there may have been life on the moon.

The moon may be an old ball of rock, but without it, our sky would not be nearly as interesting.

Turn the page.

Answer the questions below.

1 Why can no sounds be heard on the moon?

○ because sound needs air to move through

○ because there is no wind on the moon

○ because nothing happens there

○ because the moon is too far away

2 What conclusion can you draw from this selection?

○ The moon would be a good place for humans to live.

○ Earth's moon is very much like Earth.

○ The moon would seem quiet and dark to a human.

○ Life on the moon has never been possible.

3 How do we know the age of the moon?

○ Astronauts traveled to the moon to see how old it was.

○ Scientists studied rocks brought back from the moon.

○ Scientists studied the astronauts who had been to the moon.

○ We know the moon is older than Earth.

4 What is one reason astronauts need to wear spacesuits on the moon?

_____

_____

_____

_____

_____

5 What would happen to the moon's sky if the moon had air?

_____

_____

_____

_____

_____

_____

© Pearson Education 3

Read the selection. Then answer the questions that follow.

George Wins a Ride

George was excited! A few weeks before, firefighters had come to his school. They talked about how to keep homes safe from fires. They also talked about a contest. To enter the contest, students had to write about how to stay safe if there was a fire in their home.

George did not think he could win. It was his mom and dad who told him to try. He talked to his mom about what to do in case of a fire at home. Then he wrote down his ideas.

When George heard his name called as the winner, he could not sit still. He was going to be the only student who got to ride in the fire truck!

Turn the page.

Answer the questions below.

1 Why did the author write this story?

○ to persuade the reader to enter a contest

○ to entertain the reader with a story about a contest

○ to encourage the reader to write about fires

○ to explain how to be safe in case of a fire

2 Why do you think the author included a contest in the story?

○ to surprise the reader

○ to tell how people should act if they want to win a contest

○ to make the story exciting

○ to explain what a contest is

3 What is the big idea of the story?

○ You can't win if you don't try.

○ It's important to know how to be safe.

○ It's fun to ride in a fire truck.

○ Firefighters came to the school.

4 Why did the author begin by saying that George was excited?

_____

_____

_____

_____

_____

_____

_____

_____

_____

_____

_____

Read the selection. Then answer the questions that follow.

Lauren's Busy Day

Lauren had many things to do every Saturday, but this Saturday was different because Lauren's family was getting ready for visitors. Everyone was busy. Lauren had extra things to do, too, and she was worried because she could not decide what to do first. Lauren's mom told her to make a list and put her jobs in order of importance.

First, Lauren decided to write on her list the two things she did every Saturday. Every Saturday Lauren had to put away all her toys and hang up her clothes. So she wrote "clean my room" at the top of her list.

Next, Lauren wrote "clean the fish tank," because it was her job to make sure that the fish had a clean house too.

This week, Lauren's extra job was to make the extra bed for her friend who was coming to stay for the weekend. Lauren wrote "make bed" next on her list. Lauren also wanted to make a card welcoming her friend when she arrived. "Make card" was next on the list. Lauren was surprised that she was starting to feel better.

Lauren's mom came into her bedroom and saw the list. Mom wrote "have fun" at the bottom of the list. Lauren laughed and said that having fun did not need to be on her list because she never forgot to do that.

Turn the page.

Answer the questions below.

1 Why did the author write this story?

○ to describe how Lauren felt

○ to tell the reader how to make a list

○ to explain how to get ready for visitors

○ to entertain the reader with a story that teaches a lesson

2 What is the big idea of the story?

○ Get help if you are making a list.

○ Having friends visit is fun.

○ Getting ready for friends is hard work.

○ Making a list helps you get jobs done.

3 The author uses the word *surprised* in paragraph four to show that

○ feeling better can sometimes be surprising.

○ making a list is surprising.

○ Lauren felt worse after she made a list.

○ Lauren did not expect that making a list would make her feel better.

4 What is the author's purpose in the last paragraph?

○ to tell how to remember important things

○ to show that Lauren enjoyed doing her jobs

○ to describe Lauren's clean room

○ to persuade people to have more fun in their lives

5 What is the author's purpose in the fourth paragraph?

_____

_____

_____

_____

_____

_____

_____

Read the selection. Then answer the questions that follow.

Racing with Turtle

Turtle was very surprised when he beat Rabbit in the big race. After the race, photographers took Turtle's picture and reporters asked him what he did to win the race. Turtle knew he won not because he ran fast, but because he was a slow and steady runner. However, Turtle did not want to say that he was slow, so he told the reporters that he practiced running every day, ate only healthful food, and got plenty of sleep every night. Pretty soon some very important people wanted to put Turtle's picture on a cereal box. Turtle agreed.

After the big race, Rabbit felt sad because he knew he could run faster than Turtle. Rabbit's friends tried to make him feel better by saying, "Good things never happen to people who are too proud to do the right thing. Call Turtle," they said. "It will make you feel better." So Rabbit did. But when Turtle answered the phone he was rude and said, "I don't have time to talk now."

Rabbit never ran in a race again. Instead he opened a shoe store and helped people choose shoes that would help them run fast.

By now Turtle was famous, and when Snail asked Turtle to race, Turtle thought, "I can't lose."

Snail was a steady runner, but he also bought some running shoes from Rabbit that helped him run faster.

Rabbit came to watch the race. When he saw Snail and Turtle, Rabbit waved to both, but only Snail waved back.

Of course, Snail won the race.

Turn the page.

Answer the questions below.

1 Why did the author write this story?

- ○ to entertain the reader with a story that teaches a lesson about pride
- ○ to explain how to win races
- ○ to describe a feeling about racing
- ○ to persuade runners to buy good shoes

2 What is the big idea of this story?

- ○ Always look before you leap.
- ○ Bigger is not always better.
- ○ Being too proud can hurt you.
- ○ No pain, no gain

3 Why did the author choose a rabbit to race a turtle?

- ○ because turtles are known to be stupid animals
- ○ because rabbits and turtles are both good runners
- ○ because rabbits and turtles are natural enemies
- ○ because rabbits are usually faster than turtles

4 What is one way the author shows that Rabbit is no longer too proud?

_____

_____

_____

_____

5 What clue does the author give that Turtle might lose the second race?

_____

_____

_____

_____

Read the selection. Then answer the questions that follow.

Imogene

The coloring books were in place, and the crayon box was full of sharp new crayons. Imogene's favorite game was next to her favorite stuffed animal. Gus was ready. Mom had to go the store, so she asked Gus to take care of Imogene. Imogene would soon be awake. Gus looked at the toys again.

When Gus heard Imogene walking down the stairs, he stood up to meet her. Imogene saw Gus, and she laughed with delight. Gus smiled and took her hand.

"What do you want to do first?" Gus asked.

Imogene's eyes became wide as she picked up the box of crayons.

"I thought you would want to color first," said Gus.

Gus smiled as Imogene sat on the floor and started coloring the pictures.

Turn the page.

Answer the questions below.

1 You can tell from the story that Imogene is probably

○ Gus's twin sister.

○ Gus's younger sister.

○ Gus's neighbor.

○ a friend of Gus's sister.

2 Why did the author begin by describing the way Gus had arranged the toys?

○ to interest the reader in caring for small children

○ to show the reader how to arrange toys for small children

○ to show how much care Gus took to make Imogene happy

○ to show that Gus wanted to play with Imogene's toys

3 Why do you think Imogene laughed with delight when she saw Gus?

○ because she knew Gus would read her a story

○ because she knew Gus had crayons

○ because she liked to play with Gus

○ because Gus made a funny face

4 Why do you think Gus knew what kinds of toys Imogene liked?

_____

_____

_____

_____

_____

_____

_____

_____

_____

_____

Read the selection. Then answer the questions that follow.

The History Book

Ladonna felt sick. She had lost her new history book while playing with her friends after school. She had put the book down when it was her turn to kick the ball. Then she forgot to pick it up after the game. Now, as she walked home, thinking about telling her mom what had happened made her feel even more sick.

It wasn't long before Mom asked, "Where's your new book?"

"I left it at school," Ladonna said, pretending her shoe needed tying. She felt hot and sick as she answered, but Mom did not notice.

The next day when everyone was at recess, Ladonna saw a history book just like hers lying on the floor. She opened it and saw Naomi's name printed on the inside cover. Naomi was Ladonna's friend, but Ladonna was so worried about what Mom would say that she erased Naomi's name and printed her own.

Later, Ladonna could not look at Naomi. She knew she couldn't pretend that the book was hers, so she put it back where she found it.

When Ladonna got home she said, "Mom, I lost my history book." She told her mom the truth, even about taking Naomi's book. Ladonna felt better after she told her mom everything that had happened. She promised to tell Naomi what she had done, and Mom promised to help her get a new book.

© Pearson Education 3

Turn the page.

Answer the questions below.

1 Why did Ladonna feel she could not look at Naomi?

- ○ She felt sick all day.
- ○ She felt ashamed.
- ○ She could not find Naomi.
- ○ Naomi would not look at her.

2 Why did Ladonna's mom promise to help her get a new book?

- ○ because she was glad Ladonna told the truth
- ○ because Ladonna needed the book right away
- ○ because she wanted to see the new book
- ○ because Ladonna promised to give the book to Naomi

3 What is the main reason the author wrote this story?

- ○ to teach the reader to be careful with history books
- ○ to explain how to take care of schoolbooks
- ○ to express feelings about two friends at school
- ○ to teach a lesson about lying

4 Why did Ladonna feel hot and sick when she told Mom that her book was at school?

- ○ because she was sick and it was making her feel hot
- ○ because she knew she was not telling the truth
- ○ because she had gotten hot playing with her friends
- ○ because she was tying her shoe

5 How do you think the author wants you to feel about Ladonna? Explain your answer.

_____

_____

_____

_____

_____

_____

_____

_____

Read the selection. Then answer the questions that follow.

Now You See Them, Now You Don't

Did you ever wish you could disappear? Some animals can hide, change their color, or look like something else so well that it looks as if they have disappeared. How an animal "disappears" depends on what it is and where it lives. A deer can't disappear in the same way a fish can.

Most animals hide to protect themselves from other animals, and a good way for an animal to hide is to match its looks to its environment. When a deer lies on the ground, it almost disappears because the deer is brown just like the ground. A squirrel climbs a tree when it wants to disappear because its fur is brown and rough like the tree bark.

Some animals change color when the season changes. In winter, Arctic foxes are white; but in summer, their fur turns dark to match the bare ground.

Other animals use their bodies or designs on their bodies to help them blend into their natural surroundings. When some creatures are hungry, they might overlook the insect called a walking stick because it looks like a tiny branch on a tree. Some fish that live in tall grass underwater have fins that look like swaying grass. When other fish swim by, they see only tall grass.

The next time you think there are no animals around, remember to look for those that might have disappeared.

Turn the page.

Answer the questions below.

1 Why is looking like a tree branch important to a walking stick?

- ○ so that it can protect itself
- ○ so that it can scare other insects
- ○ so that it is shaped like a leaf
- ○ so that other insects will see it

2 Why does an Arctic fox's fur turn white in the winter?

- ○ so that it can be seen in the dark
- ○ so that it will be warmer
- ○ so that it will not be seen in the snow
- ○ because white fur reflects the sun

3 Why did the author write this selection?

- ○ to tell a story about animals and where they live
- ○ to explain how animals protect themselves
- ○ to describe how people can learn from animals
- ○ to express feelings about the way animals live

4 What does the author mean by "animals disappear"?

_____

_____

_____

_____

_____

5 How does the author think you can "look for animals that have disappeared"?

_____

_____

_____

_____

_____

_____

Read the selection. Then answer the questions that follow.

Clever Foxes

Foxes are clever animals. They can feel at home either in the city or on a farm. Some animals cannot live where people live, but foxes do not mind if people live near them.

Foxes do not need to hunt for just the right kind of food. Foxes have been seen eating pizza! If they are not hungry, foxes will hide food. They dig a hole and put the food in the hole to eat later.

Foxes hunt at night. A good time to see them is when the sun is just coming up or going down. The next time you want to watch a beautiful and clever animal, keep your eyes open for a fox.

Turn the page.

Answer the questions below.

1 **What is true of all foxes?**
- ○ They will eat almost anything.
- ○ They hunt in the daytime.
- ○ They live only in the country.
- ○ They do not live where people live.

2 **What does this selection tell you about how foxes hunt?**
- ○ They look for holes to hide in.
- ○ They like to eat chickens.
- ○ They hunt at night.
- ○ They hunt for food during the day.

3 **In what way are foxes like squirrels?**
- ○ Both live mostly in city parks.
- ○ Both eat other small animals.
- ○ Both are afraid to live near humans.
- ○ Both will hide food to eat later.

4 **Give one reason you think foxes are clever animals.**

_____

_____

_____

_____

_____

_____

_____

_____

_____

_____

Read the selection. Then answer the questions that follow.

Quack, Quack

Ducks are birds that are suited for the water. They have feet that look like paddles. These make ducks very good swimmers. Their feet do not have nerves or blood, so they never feel cold. Also, ducks have feathers that do not get wet because of a special oil that keeps their feathers dry.

The shape of a duck's bill, or mouth, tells how the duck gets its food. Some ducks have broad bills that help them sift the mud for insects and snails. Other ducks have long, narrow bills with sharp edges inside. These ducks catch and eat fish. If a duck's bill is wide and short, it eats plants and insects that it finds on or under the water.

Ducks are not only beautiful, but also useful to people. Some give us eggs and meat, while others give us feathers for pillows and blankets. The feathers make the pillows soft and the blankets warm.

There are hundreds of types of ducks living in ponds, rivers, oceans, and marshes all over the world. The next time you see a duck, look at its bill to notice how it eats. Remember to say thanks for the soft pillow.

Turn the page.

Answer the questions below.

1 **What is one thing you can say about all ducks?**
- ○ They have broad bills.
- ○ They can swim.
- ○ They eat insects.
- ○ They eat plants.

2 **What is true of all ducks that have long, narrow bills with sharp edges?**
- ○ They live only in rivers.
- ○ They have clawed feet.
- ○ They catch and eat fish.
- ○ They go south for the winter.

3 **What does this selection tell you about where ducks live?**
- ○ They can live in either cold or warm water.
- ○ They get most of their food by living in marshes.
- ○ They have to get out of the water to stay warm.
- ○ They would rather be on the ground than in the water.

4 **In what way are ducks like other birds?**
- ○ Both have sharp teeth and beaks.
- ○ Both live in dens and on nests.
- ○ Both eat only fish and insects.
- ○ Both have feathers and can fly.

5 **Why would someone want to raise ducks for a living?**

_____

_____

_____

_____

_____

_____

_____

Read the selection. Then answer the questions that follow.

The Cold Really Is Common

Every person you know has probably had a cold, even you. Colds are one of the most common reasons people see their doctors. Colds are also a main reason people miss work and school.

Children in school get about six to ten colds every year. If there are many children in one family, they can get as many as twelve colds every year. Doctors believe that children in school get more colds because they work together in one room, so germs spread easily.

Some people once thought that you could catch a cold if the weather outside was cold, but this is not true. We know that one way to catch a cold is to touch something that has cold germs on it and then touch your eyes or nose. You can also get a cold if someone with a cold sneezes and you breathe in the germs.

One thing you can do to stay healthy is to wash your hands often. This will kill any germs that might be on your hands. You can help keep other people healthy by covering your mouth when you sneeze or cough.

There is no cure for the common cold, but many people are working hard to find one. Every person you know probably hopes someone will find a cure soon.

Turn the page.

Answer the questions below.

1 After reading this selection, what can you say about most people and colds?

○ They work hard to find a cure for the cold.

○ They cover their mouths when they cough.

○ They wash their hands often.

○ They have had a cold.

2 Which clue word in paragraph one helps you make a generalization about people and colds?

○ every

○ person

○ hopes

○ someone

3 What is most likely true of children who have many colds every year?

○ They live where the weather changes a lot.

○ They do not go to the doctor often enough.

○ They live and work with other children who have colds.

○ Their parents don't dress them warmly enough.

4 What is one thing you can say about all people who catch colds?

_____

_____

_____

_____

5 What can you say about all people who cover their mouths when they sneeze?

_____

_____

_____

_____

_____

Read the selection. Then answer the questions that follow.

Barry's New House

Barry's family is moving to a new house today. Barry sat on his bed with his hands in his lap. Mom came into Barry's room to get more things to pack into boxes.

"I don't want to move," Barry said.

"I know how you feel," Mom said. She told Barry that she was going to miss the house and her friends. She was very nervous, too, because now she had to make new friends. Barry was surprised. He wondered if parents feel scared about moving too.

Barry walked over to Mom. She had her hands in her lap.

"Don't worry, Mom," Barry said. "You'll make new friends."

"You're right. Thank you for reminding me," Mom said.

Barry and Mom talked about moving to a new place as they packed up Barry's toys and clothes together.

Turn the page.

Answer the questions below.

1 How did Barry's feelings change from the beginning to the end of the story?

○ First, he was scared, but then he got angry.

○ First, he was asleep, but then he woke up.

○ First, he was upset, but then he felt better.

○ First, he was sad, but then he felt hungry.

2 What is the main reason the author wrote this story?

○ to explain how to move to a new house

○ to describe how Barry's mom felt about moving

○ to explain how sharing feelings can help people

○ to tell you to get help when you are planning to move

3 What is one way Barry and Mom are alike?

○ Both try to make each other feel better.

○ Both are tired of packing boxes.

○ Both are surprised about moving.

○ Both are looking forward to their new home.

4 Why is Barry surprised at what Mom said?

_____

_____

_____

_____

_____

_____

_____

_____

_____

_____

_____

_____

Read the selection. Then answer the questions that follow.

Bees and Wasps

You probably know that both bees and wasps can sting, but what else do you know about them? Did you know that after a bee stings you, the bee dies? This happens because the stinger gets stuck in you. Pulling it out means the bee would lose part of its body. A wasp can pull out its stinger and sting someone else—or sting you again.

Did you know that both bees and wasps make nests? Bees' nests are called honeycombs, and bees use them to store their food as well as to take care of baby bees. Wasps do not make honey, and they use their nests only for taking care of baby wasps.

How many insects can make their own food? Bees collect pollen and turn it into honey, which bees eat. Bees can also communicate with each other. They talk by dancing, or moving their wings and bodies in special ways. When one bee finds a good place to collect pollen, it will fly back to the nest and dance to tell the other bees.

Wasps don't make honey. Instead, they eat other insects. They may also drink nectar from flowers.

If a bee or a wasp comes buzzing around your head, just stand still and give it a chance to fly away. It is probably just curious about you.

Turn the page.

Answer the questions below.

1 What is the difference between a bee sting and a wasp sting?

○ Bees do not sting unless they are hungry.

○ Wasps can sting more than once.

○ A bee sting hurts more than a wasp sting.

○ Wasps die after they sting someone.

2 What is one way that bees' and wasps' nests are different?

○ Bees build a nest, but wasps do not.

○ Bees make their own food, but wasps hide it in nests.

○ Bees store food in their nests, but wasps do not.

○ Bees raise their babies in nests, but wasps do not.

3 What is the main reason the author wrote this selection?

○ to tell a story about bees and wasps

○ to warn you to stay away from bees and wasps

○ to describe where bees and wasps live

○ to give information about bees and wasps

4 What would wasps eat that bees would not eat?

○ flowers

○ ants

○ grass

○ honey

5 Write two things that bees and wasps have in common.

_____

_____

_____

_____

_____

_____

_____

Read the selection. Then answer the questions that follow.

Nancy and Lisa

A long time ago there were two mice, a city mouse and a country mouse. One day the city mouse, Nancy, came to visit the country mouse, Lisa. Nancy looked around Lisa's cozy hole on the side of the hill. Nancy said that it was not very big and that the tables and chairs had scratches and looked old. Lisa just smiled and told Nancy that the furniture had belonged to her mother and that it reminded her of her mom.

"I prefer new things," said Nancy.

"Let's have a snack," Lisa said, and she put some nuts and corn on the old table. They sat down on the comfortable chairs and ate peacefully.

The next week, Lisa went to visit Nancy in the city. When she got to Nancy's hole in the wall, Nancy told her to sneak in quickly because of the cat. Lisa had never seen a cat before. Suddenly a huge creature jumped at her, but luckily Lisa was close enough to the hole to escape danger. Lisa still felt nervous when they sat down in Nancy's fancy new chairs at her fancy new table. Nancy put cheese and fruit on the table, but the cat kept clawing at the hole, making so much noise that Lisa could not eat. Nancy could.

When Lisa got home, all she said was, "It's good to be home again."

© Pearson Education 3

Turn the page.

Answer the questions below.

1 **Why do you think Lisa could not eat Nancy's food but Nancy could?**

   ○ Lisa did not like fruit and cheese.

   ○ Nancy was not scared of the cat.

   ○ Lisa was tired after her long trip.

   ○ Nancy was happy with her new furniture.

2 **Why did the author write this story?**

   ○ to explain nature

   ○ to teach a lesson about differences

   ○ to make you laugh

   ○ to describe homes

3 **How are Lisa's and Nancy's homes the same?**

   ○ Both are holes in a wall.

   ○ Both are guarded by a cat.

   ○ Both have old furniture.

   ○ Both are hiding places.

4 **What were the differences between Lisa's and Nancy's chairs?**

_____

_____

_____

_____

5 **In this story, how are the country and the city different?**

_____

_____

_____

_____

Read the selection. Then answer the questions that follow.

The Planet Ocean

Our oceans were formed when Earth was very young. At first, our planet was very hot. Water did not exist in such heat because it would have boiled away. Then volcanoes filled the sky with steam. When Earth cooled down, the steam turned into water, and it rained on Earth for many, many years. This process created the first oceans.

Today, there are four or five oceans on Earth. The number is hard to say because it depends on how they are divided. The world's oceans are all connected. The same water runs through them all.

The oceans cover more than seventy percent of Earth's surface. Maybe we should call our planet Ocean instead of Earth.

Turn the page.

Answer the questions below.

1 **What happened long ago when Earth cooled down?**

   ○ The steam turned into water.

   ○ Water did not exist.

   ○ There were four or five oceans.

   ○ Oceans covered seventy percent of Earth.

2 **What happened after the steam turned into water?**

   ○ The oceans were created because of the rain.

   ○ Earth became very hot.

   ○ It began to snow.

   ○ Water boiled away.

3 **What caused the oceans to form?**

   ○ It rained on Earth for many, many years.

   ○ The world's oceans are all connected.

   ○ Earth was very hot and water boiled away.

   ○ There were no rivers or lakes on Earth.

4 **How did the volcanoes help to form the oceans?**

_____

_____

_____

_____

_____

_____

_____

_____

_____

_____

_____

Read the selection. Then answer the questions that follow.

Sea Horses

Sea horses are not really horses that live in the sea. Instead, they are tiny animals that live in the ocean near reefs and seaweed. They are the only ocean animals that swim standing up.

Sea horses look as if they were created from the body parts of other animals. The head of a sea horse looks like a horse's head. The eyes are like the eyes of a lizard; each eye can move in a different direction. A sea horse has a pocket like a kangaroo and a tail like a monkey.

Crabs, turtles, birds, and fish all eat sea horses. In order to protect itself, a sea horse can change color in an instant. It can also hide by holding on to seaweed with its tail. Finally, a sea horse has a hard, bony shell on its body for protection. Because the shell is so heavy, sea horses are not good swimmers. They rest most of the day by anchoring themselves with their tails.

A sea horse carries its eggs in its pocket. The female sea horse gives the eggs to the male sea horse, and the male carries them for three to six weeks. After the baby sea horses are born, they swim away and live on their own.

Sea horses are one of the ocean's amazing animals.

Turn the page.

- -

Answer the questions below.

1 Why do sea horses need many ways to protect themselves?

  ○ because they live in the ocean

  ○ because they look like many different animals

  ○ because they carry their babies in a pocket

  ○ because many creatures eat them

2 Why does a sea horse change color?

  ○ because seaweed changes color

  ○ because it is in danger

  ○ because it is an amazing animal

  ○ because it wants to look like other animals

3 Why does a sea horse need to rest most of the day?

  ○ because the eggs in its pocket are heavy

  ○ because it swims standing up

  ○ because its shell is heavy

  ○ because it is difficult to hold on to seaweed

4 What do baby sea horses do right after they are born?

  ○ go in search of food

  ○ look for other sea horses

  ○ hide in the male's pocket

  ○ grow a pocket and a tail

5 Why do you think sea horses live near reefs and seaweed?

_____

_____

_____

_____

_____

_____

_____

Read the selection. Then answer the questions that follow.

Look, No Cavities!

Every day, your mom probably tells you to eat your vegetables, go to bed early, and brush your teeth. Your mom knows that brushing your teeth removes the bacteria that can cause tiny holes, or cavities, in your teeth. More people have cavities today than ever before because we eat so much sugar.

There are things you can do to help prevent cavities, but once you have one, it is time to visit the dentist. To repair a cavity, a dentist must first drill a hole in the tooth and clean out the decay. The dentist then fills the hole and seals it. Cavities may cause pain if they become too deep.

Your mom and your dentist know that brushing is the best way to stop a cavity from starting. Dentists say that you should brush your teeth for as long as a song on the radio plays, or about three minutes. If you eat and can't brush your teeth right away, rinsing your mouth with water helps remove the food that gives bacteria a place to start growing. Of course, eating less sugar also helps prevent cavities.

Remember, the next time your mom reminds you to brush your teeth, just turn on the radio and start brushing.

Turn the page.

Answer the questions below.

1 What is the main reason people today have so many cavities?

- ○ They eat so much sugar.
- ○ They do not brush their teeth.
- ○ They do not go to the dentist.
- ○ There are so many bacteria today.

2 Before a dentist can fill a cavity, what must happen?

- ○ The cavity must be sealed.
- ○ The decay must be cleaned out.
- ○ The teeth must be brushed.
- ○ The cavity may cause pain.

3 Why is rinsing your teeth not as good as brushing them?

- ○ because you can never rinse your mouth long enough
- ○ because water isn't healthy
- ○ because sometimes you can't rinse after you eat
- ○ because rinsing does not get rid of bacteria

4 Why do you think dentists say you should brush for as long as one song on the radio plays?

_____

_____

_____

_____

5 What are the two best ways to prevent cavities?

_____

_____

_____

_____

Read the selection. Then answer the questions that follow.

Something Fishy

When you think of fish in the ocean, do you think of dolphins? Dolphins live in the ocean, but they are not fish.

Both fish and dolphins need air to live, but they breathe differently. Fish do not have lungs. They have gills. They take in air from the water when water passes over their gills.

Dolphins have lungs like humans, so they must come to the surface of the water to get air. They have small holes on the top of their heads where the air comes in and out.

Fish and dolphins do not even swim the same way. Fish move their tails from side to side, but dolphins move their tails up and down.

Fish and dolphins are different, but both are fun to watch.

© Pearson Education 3

Turn the page.

Answer the questions below.

1 **What is one way that dolphins are like humans?**

○ They do not have lungs.

○ They cannot breathe through their noses.

○ They cannot breathe underwater.

○ They cannot swim underwater.

2 **How are dolphins, fish, and humans alike?**

○ They all have gills.

○ They all need air.

○ They all have lungs.

○ They all live in water.

3 **How can a fish breathe underwater?**

○ It gets air from the water.

○ It finds air pockets underwater.

○ It produces air by moving its tail.

○ Its heart beats fast to produce air.

4 **How do dolphins and fish move differently?**

_____

_____

_____

_____

_____

_____

_____

_____

_____

_____

Read the selection. Then answer the questions that follow.

Table Manners

People in different countries have their own ways of doing things. Even the way people eat changes from one country to another. People in China do not have the same customs as people in America.

In China, people use chopsticks to eat. Chopsticks are a pair of long, thin, wooden sticks that take the place of a fork. There is a special way to hold them, using the fingers of one hand. People who usually use a fork need to practice using chopsticks.

Just as with a knife and fork, you should not put your chopsticks just anywhere when you finish eating. You should lay the chopsticks across the top of the rice bowl, which also shows that you have finished eating. If you place the chopsticks straight up in a bowl of rice, people will think you wish them bad luck. This is because when someone dies in China, it is the custom to place two sticks of incense upright in a bowl of rice or in sand on a shrine.

There is also a proper way to place a teapot on the table. The spout should not point toward anyone, but toward a place where nobody is sitting.

Whether you use chopsticks or forks, it is always polite to thank the cook after you eat.

Turn the page.

Answer the questions below.

1 **How are chopsticks and a fork alike?**
- ○ They are both used to pick up food.
- ○ They are both made of wood.
- ○ They are both used mostly in China.
- ○ They are both placed across a bowl of rice.

2 **What is one way that chopsticks are different from a fork?**
- ○ You can pick up more food with chopsticks.
- ○ You can use chopsticks with one hand.
- ○ You can eat faster with chopsticks.
- ○ You need two chopsticks to pick up food.

3 **How are eating customs in China and America similar?**
- ○ The people in both countries use a fork.
- ○ People in both countries place their eating utensils in a special place after eating.
- ○ The people in both countries eat only rice.
- ○ The people in both countries put a teapot on the table at every meal.

4 **According to some people in China, what happens when chopsticks are placed straight up in a bowl of rice?**
- ○ The rice will be spoiled.
- ○ You can't eat the rice.
- ○ It brings bad luck.
- ○ The chopsticks will be ruined.

5 **Besides eating, what is another custom that may be different in China and America?**

_____

_____

_____

_____

_____

_____

Read the selection. Then answer the questions that follow.

Biomes

A biome is an area of the world where the environment determines the type of plants and animals that live there. Deserts and tropical rain forests are biomes that you probably know about. However, you may not know about tundra and taiga, which are biomes in the northern part of the world.

Tundra is the coldest and driest biome on Earth. There are no trees and not many plants because the ground is always frozen. Because tundra is located far north, the position of the sun creates nights that may last as long as two months in the winter and a day in summer that may last almost twenty-four hours. Animals such as deer, rabbits, and wolves can live in the tundra biome. Some birds live there in the summer, and some fish can live in the cold water.

Taiga is south of the tundra biome, so it is not as cold. There are few plants in taiga, but evergreens can grow tall because they have a covering on their needles that protects them from the cold. Taiga is home to many of the same kinds of animals and birds that live in the tundra biome. In the summer, millions of insects live on tundra and taiga. They provide food for birds.

Tundra and taiga are home to some plants and animals that can't live anywhere else, which makes these biomes valuable to our planet.

Turn the page.

Answer the questions below.

1 How is tundra like taiga?
- ○ Only animals live there in the summer.
- ○ Many of the same animals live there.
- ○ Both have thick evergreen forests.
- ○ On both, the ground is always frozen.

2 How is tundra different from taiga?
- ○ Tundra does not have summer.
- ○ Tundra does not have trees.
- ○ Tundra does not have animal life.
- ○ Tundra is not as cold as taiga.

3 What is one reason more birds live on taiga in summer than in winter?
- ○ The days are longer.
- ○ The weather is colder.
- ○ There are more trees.
- ○ There is more to eat.

4 What is a major difference between the tundra biome and a tropical rain forest?

_____

_____

_____

_____

5 How is the tundra biome like a desert?

_____

_____

_____

_____

Read the selection. Then answer the questions that follow.

The Day Off

David's school was closed today because of the snowstorm the night before. Soon David and his friends were on their way to a nearby hill for some sledding. The path was covered with snow and ice, so the boys had to be careful. However, they had a great time for most of the day.

When David got back home, his dad told him how lucky they were. Their lights were still on and their house was warm. Most other houses in town were cold and dark.

David's dad did not drive to work today. Many people did, and their cars slid into trees, fences, and even other cars.

David felt better when his dad told him not to worry because the storm was over now.

Turn the page.

Answer the questions below.

1 What was true of most houses in town after the storm?

○ The houses were warm.

○ The houses were cold.

○ The houses were empty.

○ The houses were old.

2 Why do you think David's dad did not drive to work?

○ His car would not start.

○ He wanted to go sledding.

○ He was sick.

○ The roads were very icy.

3 What can you say about many people who drove to work after the storm?

○ They drove their cars too fast.

○ They got into car accidents.

○ Their children went to school.

○ Their children were David's friends.

4 How do you think David and his friends felt about the storm?

_____

_____

_____

_____

_____

_____

_____

_____

_____

_____

_____

Read the selection. Then answer the questions that follow.

Deserts

Many people think that deserts are very hot places where nothing can live, but this is not true. Some deserts get very cold when the sun goes down, and some plants and animals can live in the hottest and coldest of these deserts.

Deserts are places that get less than ten to twenty inches of rain per year. To give you an idea, most of Florida usually gets more than fifty inches of rain each year. Some desert areas may go as long as a year without any rain.

Because deserts are so dry, the animals that live there must be able to live without much water. The animals adapt to this condition in different ways. Some insects and toads dig holes in the sand and hide during the day. This keeps them from getting thirsty because they are not in the hot sun. Some toads can hide in holes for up to eight months. They come out only when it rains. Rats and coyotes sleep during the day and hunt for food at night when the desert is cooler.

Plants live in the desert too. Many, like the cactus, have spines instead of leaves, which help them retain water. A cactus can store water in its stem and roots. It has broad, shallow roots that catch rain when it falls. Other plants have very deep roots that allow them to reach water far under the ground.

Turn the page.

Answer the questions below.

1 **How do animals in hot, dry places live without much water?**

  ○ They try to stay cool.

  ○ They only go out during the day.

  ○ They look for water in other places.

  ○ They sleep most of the time.

2 **Why does a cactus plant store water in its stem and roots?**

  ○ so that it can breathe

  ○ so that it can grow leaves

  ○ so that it can survive in its dry surroundings

  ○ so that it can hide during the day

3 **Which statement is true of all desert animals?**

  ○ They are always hungry because there is little food.

  ○ They come out of hiding only when it rains.

  ○ They move around a lot if it gets too hot and dry.

  ○ They have learned how to live without much water.

4 **Which statement is true of most deserts?**

  ○ They get at least twenty inches of rain each year.

  ○ They get no rain, and no plants can grow there.

  ○ They get less than twenty inches of rain each year.

  ○ They get rain only once or twice each year.

5 **What do most desert plants and animals have in common?**

_____

_____

_____

_____

_____

_____

_____

Read the selection. Then answer the questions that follow.

Art from the Garden

People have been using gourds for thousands of years to carry water, make

music, and play games. Today gourds are also used for crafts and fine artwork.

Anyone can grow gourds, even without much land, because gourds grow on vines

that can be trained to grow up poles or fences. After the gourd is grown, it can be

dried so that only the seeds are left inside, which makes it very light.

Gourds are perfect for crafts because they have the look and feel of wood, and

they come in all shapes and sizes. Artists can paint, carve, cut, and burn gourds.

Because no two gourds are ever the same, each one gives the artist a new idea for

how to design and use it.

Gourd birdhouses can be plain or carved and painted. Gourd bowls can be

polished and decorated with leaves or pine needles. Gourds can be carved, cut,

and painted to make baskets. With straps attached, gourds make elegant purses.

These crafts are so beautiful that it's impossible to tell they were once growing in a

garden.

Because gourds are easy to grow and can last almost forever, they are a popular

way for people to make beautiful and useful items.

Turn the page.

Answer the questions below.

1 **What is probably true of most people who work with gourds?**

○ They are famous artists.

○ They like to work with their hands.

○ They are better gardeners than artists.

○ They like to paint more than to carve.

2 **Which statement is true of most gourds?**

○ They are easy to grow and work with.

○ They are big because they grow on vines.

○ Only fine artists can work with them.

○ They look and feel like baskets.

3 **What happens to make gourds light and easy to work with?**

○ They shrink.

○ They lose their seeds.

○ The inside dries up.

○ They come off the vine.

4 **Why do many artists like to work with gourds?**

_____

_____

_____

_____

_____

5 **What is true of many items made from gourds?**

_____

_____

_____

_____

_____

Read the selection. Then answer the questions that follow.

Bicycle Safety

Riding a bicycle is the best way to have fun, but you should always wear something to protect your head. Many states have laws about bicycle safety. Your state may require you to wear a helmet when you ride. You should learn about the safety laws in your state.

The best kind of helmet should sit straight on your head and make contact with your head at all times. If you can move the helmet after you buckle the strap, it is not a good fit. Red helmets look the best.

Most helmets are padded and have a thin plastic cover. The plastic will make the helmet slide on the hard ground if you should fall. This protects your head and neck. Helmets do not cost a lot of money.

No matter when or where you ride a bicycle, be safe and wear a helmet.

Turn the page.

Answer the questions below.

1 The first sentence in the selection is a statement of opinion. How do you know?
- ◯ because the first sentence is usually an opinion
- ◯ because it tells how only one person feels about riding bicycles
- ◯ because a person did not say it
- ◯ because bicycles are not made just for fun

2 Which sentence from the selection is a statement of fact?
- ◯ Many states have laws about bicycle saftey.
- ◯ Red helmets look the best.
- ◯ Helmets do not cost a lot of money.
- ◯ Be safe and wear a helmet.

3 What is true of most bicycle helmets?
- ◯ The best helmets are red.
- ◯ All bicycle riders wear them.
- ◯ The outside of the helmet is plastic.
- ◯ They should not touch the head.

4 Write a statement of fact from the third paragraph.

_____

_____

_____

_____

_____

_____

_____

_____

_____

_____

Read the selection. Then answer the questions that follow.

Settlers' Lights

Today, people can buy candles with different shapes, colors, sizes, and even smells, although we no longer need to use candles as a main source of light. Years ago, settlers worked hard to light their cabins, and they did not worry about how candles looked or smelled. Making candles was a dirty job that took hours, so people were happy to have any kind of candle.

Many years ago, people made candles from the fat of the animals they killed for food. They melted the fat, boiled it in water, strained it, and then cooled it. Some people added spices to the hot fat so that it would not smell bad.

Dipping was an easy way to make candles. String was dipped into the hot fat, taken out, and then cooled. The string was dipped and cooled many times, each time adding another layer of fat, until the candle was the desired size. Even children enjoyed dipping candles.

Some settlers used molds that looked like tall metal boxes with holes at the top. Strings were put into the holes, and hot fat was poured in. The candles were cooled and then taken out. Molds were not as messy as dipping, and one person could make many candles at once.

Making candles was hard work, but having light was worth the effort.

Turn the page.

Answer the questions below.

1 **Which sentence is a statement of fact?**

○ People made candles from the fat of animals.

○ Dipping was an easy way to make candles.

○ Children were good at dipping candles.

○ Making candles was hard work.

2 **Which sentence is a statement of opinion?**

○ Some people added spices to the hot fat.

○ Some settlers used molds that looked like tall metal boxes.

○ Molds were not as messy as dipping.

○ One person could make many candles at once.

3 **What do you think most candles the settlers made looked like?**

○ They were different sizes and shapes.

○ They were shaped like animals.

○ They were small because the cabins were small.

○ They were short and fat.

4 **How might the author know what candle molds looked like?**

○ by seeing them in a museum

○ by buying them at a store

○ by visiting a modern candle factory

○ by looking at candles made today

5 **How could you find out whether this selection contains facts?**

_____

_____

_____

_____

_____

_____

_____

Read the selection. Then answer the questions that follow.

American Hero

Cesar Chavez (1927–1993) became one of the most famous people in America by organizing migrant farm workers. These are workers who travel from farm to farm looking for work as the seasons change and different crops need to be harvested. Chavez himself was a migrant worker, so he understood what it was like to be one. His life is one of the most fascinating stories in American history.

Migrant workers did not own homes and most lived in poor conditions. The children did not attend school because families were always moving to find work. This challenging lifestyle affected migrant workers from 1938 to 1985.

As Chavez worked on the farms, he saw how unfairly the workers were being treated by the farm owners. The workers made very little money, worked long hours, and had no rights. Chavez talked about making changes.

He traveled from farm to farm teaching the workers how to read and write. He talked to them about how they could improve their lives. All the workers wanted to learn, but they were afraid they would lose their jobs if they made demands.

Chavez believed in nonviolent methods, such as marches and boycotts, to bring about change. He was very brave. By fasting, or not eating, for long periods of time, Chavez began to draw attention to the problems of migrant workers. People from around the country took notice. His strong leadership was admired and respected by all Americans.

Thanks to Cesar Chavez, the lives of many migrant farm workers have been greatly improved.

Turn the page.

Answer the questions below.

1 **Which sentence is a statement of fact?**
- ○ Cesar Chavez became one of the most famous people in America.
- ○ Migrant workers travel from farm to farm looking for work.
- ○ His life is one of the most fascinating stories in American history.
- ○ Cesar Chavez was a strong and able leader.

2 **Which sentence is a statement of opinion?**
- ○ Chavez was a migrant worker.
- ○ In 1945, most migrant workers did not own homes.
- ○ Cesar Chavez was very brave.
- ○ He traveled from farm to farm, teaching.

3 **Which of the following would be the best source of information about Cesar Chavez?**
- ○ a book about American farms
- ○ a biography of Cesar Chavez
- ○ a picture of Cesar Chavez
- ○ a movie about farm workers

4 **What is your opinion of Cesar Chavez? Write one sentence telling why you think as you do.**

_____

_____

_____

_____

_____

5 **Write another statement of fact about migrant farm workers.**

_____

_____

_____

_____

_____

Read the selection. Then answer the questions that follow.

Where Was Max?

Every day when Nina got home from school, her dog, Max, was waiting to say

hello, but today when she walked into her house, Max wasn't there. *Where was*

Max?

She went to her room, but Max was not under the bed.

Maybe Max was in the yard, she thought. Nina looked in the bushes and near the

porch, but she could not find Max.

Nina was worried. She went back into the house and looked at the hook where

Max's leash should have been, but it was not there. Could someone have taken him?

Just then Mom came into the house with Max on his leash. "I took Max to get

the shots he needs to stay healthy," Mom said.

"I'm glad you're both home," said Nina, and Max barked in agreement.

Turn the page.

Answer the questions below.

1　What was Nina's problem in this story?
- ○ Max's leash was missing.
- ○ Mom was not home.
- ○ She could not find Max.
- ○ Max needed his shots.

2　What is the big idea of this story?
- ○ Nina could not find her dog.
- ○ Nina had a dog named Max.
- ○ Mom took Max to the vet.
- ○ Max was supposed to be at home every day.

3　Which of the following is not an important part of the plot?
- ○ Max was not waiting for Nina when she came home.
- ○ Max barked in agreement.
- ○ Nina could not find Max in the bushes.
- ○ Mom came home with Max on a leash.

4　What can you say is usually true of Max?

_____

_____

_____

_____

_____

_____

_____

_____

_____

_____

_____

Read the selection. Then answer the questions that follow.

Addo's Poster

Addo's class was going to visit the science museum on Thursday. He knew he would want to buy the poster that showed Earth as seen by astronauts in space, but he didn't have enough money. He had already bought candy with all of his allowance money.

Addo picked up his glass Liberty Bell bank and thought about breaking it, but he saw that there were only a few nickels and dimes in it. That would not be enough for the poster.

Addo asked Mom for some money, but she reminded him about the family rule: Allowance is given every Friday. No exceptions.

Addo asked Mom what he could do to earn money before next Thursday.

"Mr. Linnet said he would pay you to feed and walk his dog," Mom said.

Addo made a deal with Mr. Linnet to walk and feed the dog every weekday. On Monday, Addo started his job. It was not a hard job, but afterward Addo had to walk home, eat dinner, and do his homework. He was very busy that week. In fact, he was so busy that he didn't have time to spend any money. When Mr. Linnet paid him on Thursday, Addo was surprised to be paid so much money.

When Addo got home he told Mom how much money he'd earned.

"You also saved that much money from your allowance," she said, smiling.

"I can buy the poster now," he said proudly.

Turn the page.

Answer the questions below.

1 **What was Addo's problem in this story?**

   ○ He did not want to work for Mr. Linnet.

   ○ He needed money to buy a poster.

   ○ His class was going to the science museum.

   ○ His allowance was too small.

2 **What did Addo learn in this story?**

   ○ Working and going to school are tiring.

   ○ If you break a rule, you will be sorry.

   ○ If you work and save money, you can buy what you want.

   ○ If you are busy, time goes by fast.

3 **Which detail is important to the plot?**

   ○ Addo's bank looked like the Liberty Bell.

   ○ The man Addo worked for was named Mr. Linnet.

   ○ Addo started his job on Monday.

   ○ Addo's family had a rule about money.

4 **Which statement best describes the end of the story?**

   ○ Addo does not have enough money.

   ○ Addo asks Mom for some money.

   ○ Addo walks and feeds Mr. Linnet's dog.

   ○ Addo is proud and excited to buy the poster.

5 **What can you say is true about Addo?**

_____

_____

_____

_____

_____

_____

_____

© Pearson Education 3

Read the selection. Then answer the questions that follow.

Jack's Friend

Vance was a giant who lived alone in a gigantic castle. The townspeople who lived nearby feared and disliked anyone who was different. They especially disliked large people who could pick them up in one hand. So when Vance went to town, people threw rocks at him. The rocks hurt only his feelings, but he was a tender-hearted giant with sensitive feelings.

One day when Vance was out for a stroll, he nearly stumbled over a small gentleman who could only hear the giant's booming footsteps.

"You must be quite large!" said the gentleman as he turned toward the sound. "My name is Jack McGillicutty. What's yours?"

Vance was so shocked that all he could say was "Aren't you afraid of me?"

But Jack wasn't afraid. He even asked Vance to help him find the post office, which Vance was happy to do.

"Thank you, and I hope we meet again soon," said Jack. Vance mentioned that he planned to go out walking again the next day, so they agreed to meet.

The next day, Vance leaned against a mountain while Jack sat on a bench at his feet. As they talked about music, some rocks suddenly came flying at them. One of the rocks hit Jack. Vance stood up and stomped his feet, scaring all the rock-throwers away.

"Thank you, my friend," said Jack.

Vance was glad Jack could not see the tiny tear on his cheek.

"You're welcome" was all he could say.

Turn the page.

Answer the questions below.

1 **What was the problem in the story?**

○ Jack was not able to see the giant coming.

○ Vance was a giant who tormented the townspeople.

○ Vance was too sensitive, and his feelings were easily hurt.

○ The townspeople disliked Vance because he was different.

2 **What did you learn from reading the story?**

○ You need to watch where you are walking.

○ People who live in towns like to throw stones.

○ People who are different can be friends.

○ Giants cannot have any friends.

3 **Which of the following is not important to the plot of the story?**

○ Jack said he was not afraid of Vance.

○ Vance was leaning against a mountain.

○ The townspeople disliked Vance.

○ Jack and Vance were friends.

4 **Why did Vance almost stumble over Jack?**

_____

_____

_____

_____

_____

5 **What can you say about both Jack and Vance?**

_____

_____

_____

_____

_____

Read the selection. Then answer the questions that follow.

Sparrows

The song sparrow and the house sparrow are birds that look almost alike, but you can tell them apart if you know what to look for. The song sparrow and the house sparrow can be found in almost every yard in North America. The next time you see a sparrow, look at its chest. The song sparrow has a white chest with dark lines below its neck, while the house sparrow's chest does not have any lines.

Then look at its neck. All song sparrows have a white neck with two stripes on each side. But only the male house sparrow has a black neck and white cheeks.

Even their songs are not the same. A house sparrow sings "cheep, cheep." A song sparrow sings more varied notes.

The next time you see a sparrow in your yard, look at its chest and its neck. Then listen to its song. Hopefully, you will be able to see and hear the difference.

Turn the page.

Answer the questions below.

1 **How are a song sparrow and a house sparrow alike?**

○ They both live near people.

○ They both have white cheeks.

○ They both have lines on their chests.

○ They both have the same kind of song.

2 **How are a song sparrow and a house sparrow different?**

○ A song sparrow has a black neck, and a house sparrow has a white neck.

○ A song sparrow has a more varied song.

○ A house sparrow has more lines on its neck.

○ A house sparrow lives in a house, and a song sparrow lives in a yard.

3 **What can you say is true of most house and song sparrows?**

○ They live in many different places.

○ They sing the same song.

○ They are mostly white.

○ They are colorful birds.

4 **How is the chest of a song sparrow different from that of a house sparrow?**

_____

_____

_____

_____

_____

_____

_____

_____

_____

_____

Read the selection. Then answer the questions that follow.

Castles

You might think that castles exist only in fairy tales, but castles are real places that were used by real people long ago. Castles in Japan and in England did not look the same, but they were all built as forts to protect people and animals.

English castles were usually built using stone or bricks. Japanese castles were usually made of wood. In both countries castles had moats, or small rivers, around them to protect people and animals. The bridge across the moat could be pulled up to keep out unwanted people.

Both countries developed a style of castle with inner walls as well as an outer wall. This meant that an attacker who got past the outer wall would still not reach the people who lived inside.

In the center of a Japanese castle of this kind was a tower that could be well defended. The lords of the castle usually lived in the next group of buildings. The warriors lived outside the castle, but nearby in case there was an attack.

In England, living in a castle was like living in a small town. People who lived in a castle could grow or make everything they needed. Castles were always noisy because farmers raised cows and pigs, and soldiers marched there.

Today castles are not used in the same way that they were used many years ago. In each country we can visit castles and imagine how people once lived.

© Pearson Education 3

Turn the page.

Answer the questions below.

1 In both England and Japan, how were the people who lived in castles alike?

- ○ They were warriors needed to defend the castle.
- ○ They were farmers who kept cows and pigs.
- ○ They were people who wanted to be safe.
- ○ They had no other place to live.

2 What is one way that a castle in Japan was different from a castle in England?

- ○ It had a moat.
- ○ It was built as a fort.
- ○ It was built with inner and outer walls.
- ○ It was made of wood.

3 The author writes, "Castles were always noisy because farmers raised cows and pigs there." What clue word tells you that this statement is true of most English castles?

- ○ castles
- ○ always
- ○ farmers
- ○ cows

4 How are castles in Japan and England alike?

- ○ Both had inner and outer walls and moats.
- ○ Both had lords and ladies and warriors living in them.
- ○ They were made of the same materials.
- ○ They looked the same.

5 What is probably the main difference between the use of castles today and the use of castles long ago?

_____

_____

_____

_____

_____

_____

Read the selection. Then answer the questions that follow.

Role Models

Tiger Woods and Michael Jordan are two of the most famous names and faces in sports. Both men have been on magazine covers, on television, and on cereal boxes.

Michael Jordan has been called the best basketball player in the history of the game, so it's surprising to learn that when he was in high school he did not make the basketball team. However, he did not give up. He worked very hard to become a good player, and the next year he joined the team. As a professional, he was a leader for the Chicago Bulls.

Jordan's leadership extended off the court too. He opened the James R. Jordan Boys and Girls Club and Family Center, named after his father. The center gives the people of Chicago a safe place to relax and have fun.

Tiger Woods is one of the world's most famous golfers. He swung his first golf club when he was only eleven months old. He also won every junior golf tournament he entered. At eighteen, he was the youngest player ever to win the U.S. Amateur tournament, and he is the only golfer ever to win it three times in a row.

Like Michael Jordan, Tiger Woods wanted to be a role model for kids, so he created the Tiger Woods Foundation. The foundation provides opportunities for less fortunate children to participate in many types of worthwhile activities.

Jordan and Woods are two champions who also care about and help others.

Turn the page.

Answer the questions below.

1 **How are Michael Jordan and Tiger Woods alike?**

○ Both showed special talent when they were very young.

○ Both have worked hard to help other people.

○ Both were the youngest ever to win major awards.

○ Both were the highest scorers for their teams.

2 **What is one way that Michael Jordan and Tiger Woods are different?**

○ Jordan likes sports, and Woods does not.

○ Jordan played sports in high school, and Woods started in middle school.

○ Jordan plays a team sport, and Woods does not.

○ Jordan is well-known, and Woods is not.

3 **What generalization can you make about both Tiger Woods and Michael Jordan?**

○ They are concerned only about sports.

○ Not many people know them.

○ They work hard to be the best they can be.

○ They both play basketball.

4 **Which of these two athletes is your favorite? Why?**

_____

_____

_____

_____

5 **How are the organizations these two athletes started the same?**

_____

_____

_____

_____

_____

Read the selection. Then answer the questions that follow.

Popcorn

Popcorn is the best snack. It is said that Americans have been eating popcorn since it was brought to the first Thanksgiving dinner. In fact, in the early 1700s boys and girls ate popcorn with milk and sugar for breakfast.

Popcorn is easy to grow. Corn seeds are planted in warm weather. They grow into tall plants with ears of corn. The ears are picked about ten weeks after the kernels begin to grow. When the kernels are taken off the ear, the popcorn is ready to pop.

Popcorn tastes best during a movie. It also makes a beautiful holiday decoration. Birds eat popcorn too.

The next time you are hungry or want to feed the birds, you might want to pop some corn.

Turn the page.

Answer the questions below.

1 Which sentence from the selection is a statement of fact?

○ Popcorn is the best snack.

○ Corn seeds are planted in warm weather.

○ Popcorn tastes best during a movie.

○ Popcorn makes a beautiful holiday decoration.

2 Which sentence is a statement of opinion?

○ Boys and girls once ate popcorn for breakfast.

○ The ears are picked ten weeks after the kernels grow.

○ The kernels grow into tall plants with ears of corn.

○ Popcorn is easy to grow.

3 Which of the following would be the best source of information about how to grow corn?

○ a history book about Thanksgiving dinner

○ a picture of corn

○ a nonfiction book about corn

○ a movie theatre

4 How is your breakfast the same or different from some breakfasts in the 1700s?

_____

_____

_____

_____

_____

_____

_____

_____

_____

_____

Read the selection. Then answer the questions that follow.

Prickly Pear Cactus

Looking at the prickly pear cactus with its flat pads and inch-long thorns, you might think that it is not a useful plant, but you would be mistaken. People all over the world use the beautiful prickly pear cactus for many things.

Luther Burbank, a plant scientist, began studying the prickly pear cactus plants many years ago. He learned that if cactus plants are planted close together, they can grow to form a wall ten to twenty feet high. This type of wall can keep out many animals.

Like all cactus plants, the prickly pears do not need much water and can live in almost any kind of dirt. They can be planted in places that do not have many plants at all. Thus, they help keep the soil in place.

Juice from the pads of the prickly pear is very useful. If you have burned yourself, you can put the juice on the burn to make it feel better. The juice can also be used to make candles. Some people mix the juice with other materials and use it on buildings to make them last longer.

The fresh pads of a prickly pear cactus without thorns can be fed to pigs and sheep. People can also eat the pads. Prickly pear jelly, bread, and soups are delicious. Even the seeds can be dried and made into flour.

Even though the prickly pear cactus may not look like a treasure, many people think it is a gem.

Turn the page.

Answer the questions below.

1 Which of these is a statement of fact?

○ Prickly pear jelly and prickly pear soups are delicious.

○ The prickly pear cactus is beautiful.

○ The prickly pear cactus has inch-long thorns.

○ The prickly pear cactus is a gem.

2 The author writes, "Even the seeds can be dried and made into flour." Which of the following best describes this statement?

○ It is a statement of opinion.

○ It is a statement of fact.

○ It contains both a statement of fact and opinion.

○ It is a false statement.

3 According to the selection, juice from the prickly pear can be used to make candles. What would be the best way to prove that this statement of fact is true?

○ Find someone who owns a prickly pear cactus.

○ Look at a photograph of a prickly pear cactus.

○ Ask your friends.

○ Check sources that explain the uses of the prickly pear cactus.

4 How are the prickly pear cactus and all other cactus plants alike?

○ They need a special type of dirt.

○ They do not need much water to grow.

○ They were studied by Luther Burbank.

○ They grow ten to twenty feet high.

5 What is another statement of fact from the selection?

_____

_____

_____

_____

_____

_____

Read the selection. Then answer the questions that follow.

Frozen Rain

Have you ever heard of rain freezing in the summer? Well, frozen rain can fall out of a strong summer thunderstorm in the form of hail.

Hail begins as a thundercloud that contains "supercooled" water. "Supercooled" water does not freeze, even though its temperature is below freezing. The water needs to touch something solid in order to freeze. As it freezes around ice crystals, frozen raindrops, dust, or salt from the ocean, it is carried upward by wind currents and gathers more water. When the ball of ice is too heavy to remain in the cloud, it drops to the Earth as ice. The hail does not melt as it falls because it is not in the air long enough. A hailstorm is an exciting sight.

If you cut a hailstone in half, it would look like the inside of an onion. The rings give information about how the hailstorm was formed.

Most hail is smaller than a dime, but the largest hailstone was more than seventeen inches around (more than five inches in diameter) and weighed about one and a half pounds.

Although hailstorms usually last for only about fifteen minutes, they can cause a lot of damage. Hail can fall to Earth as fast as ninety miles per hour, and when it hits farm crops or windows, it can seriously damage them.

The next time you see little snowballs falling out of the sky, be sure to wait before you go outside.

Turn the page.

Answer the questions below.

1 Which sentence from the selection is a statement of opinion?

  ◯ The hail does not melt as it falls.

  ◯ The rings tell how the hailstone was formed.

  ◯ Hail can fall to Earth as fast as ninety miles per hour.

  ◯ A hailstorm is an exciting sight.

2 What would be the best way to find out if there has been a larger hailstone since this selection was written?

  ◯ Look in the dictionary.

  ◯ Check on the Internet.

  ◯ Read a book about weather forecasting.

  ◯ Watch a television program about severe weather.

3 Which of the following best describes this selection?

  ◯ It is mostly statements of fact.

  ◯ It is mostly statements of opinion.

  ◯ It contains more statements of opinion than statements of fact.

  ◯ It is all statements of opinion.

4 Why does the author compare hail to an onion?

_____

_____

_____

_____

_____

5 How does the author know that hail causes damage?

_____

_____

_____

_____

_____

Read the selection. Then answer the questions that follow.

"Ground Nut" Butter

Did you know that most nuts grow on trees? That's why peanuts are sometimes called "ground nuts." Peanuts belong to the same plant family as beans and peas. They actually grow underground.

Farmers dig up the peanuts using special machines. They leave the peanuts on the ground to dry for two days or more. Then they dry the peanuts with warm air.

Many of the dried raw peanuts are used to make peanut butter. This is how it is made. First the peanuts are taken out of their shells. Then the peanuts are roasted and cooled. A machine takes off the red skin. Then the pieces are ground up until the peanuts are smooth like butter. The peanut butter is then put into jars and sold.

The next time you ask for a sandwich, make it "ground nut" butter and jelly.

Turn the page.

Answer the questions below.

1 What is the first step in making peanut butter?

   ○ The shell is removed.

   ○ A machine takes off the red skin.

   ○ The peanuts are ground up.

   ○ The peanuts are roasted.

2 When do farmers sell the raw peanuts?

   ○ while the peanuts are in the field

   ○ after the shells are removed

   ○ after the peanuts have been dried

   ○ two days after digging them up

3 When could you ask for a "ground nut" sandwich?

   ○ after a jar of peanut butter has been sold

   ○ when the farmers dry peanuts with warm air

   ○ when the peanuts have been taken out of their shells

   ○ when the peanuts are being ground up

4 How are peanuts different from most other nuts?

_____

_____

_____

_____

_____

_____

_____

_____

_____

_____

_____

_____

Answer the questions below.

Read the selection. Then answer the questions that follow.

Build a Castle

You can build your very own castle if you have a plan and lots of sand. The next time you are on a sandy beach, just follow these simple steps.

First, imagine the kind of castle you would like to make and, if you want to, draw a diagram on a piece of paper. Then find a place to build your castle that is not too close or too far away from the water. Near your spot, dig a hole with your hands until you find sand that is very wet. This is the sand you will scoop out and use to make your castle.

Begin by making towers from the wet sand you scooped. Take some sand and shape it into a pancake, making a big pancake for the bottom and smaller pancakes as you stack them up into a tower. After you make one tower, pour water on it to seal it and keep the tower from falling apart. Then build another tower and seal that one, and keep making towers until you have as many as you want according to your diagram.

You can connect the towers by making walls between them. To make the walls, take some wet sand and shape it into a brick. Put one brick on top of another one until your wall is as high as you want.

Finally, smooth the walls and towers with a flat tool like a small sand shovel. Then step back and admire your castle.

Once the tide comes in, you will have to build a new castle all over again the next day!

© Pearson Education 3

Turn the page.

Answer the questions below.

1 In building a castle, when do you connect the towers?

○ before you make a pancake shape

○ before you stack up the pancakes

○ after you admire your castle

○ after you make two or more towers

2 What is the first step in making a sand castle?

○ finding some wet sand and scooping it up

○ thinking about what kind of castle you want

○ drawing a diagram of the castle on paper

○ finding a good place to build the castle

3 When do you use a flat tool to smooth the walls?

○ after building the walls

○ before you seal the towers

○ before you make the towers

○ while you are digging the hole

4 When should you pour water on the towers?

○ as soon as one tower dries

○ just before the towers fall

○ after you make each tower

○ after you have as many towers as you want

5 How is building a sand castle the same as building a castle made of wooden blocks?

_____

_____

_____

_____

_____

_____

_____

Read the selection. Then answer the questions that follow.

Ready to Cook

Cooking can be fun, and following some simple rules and ideas will help you.

Once you decide what you want to make, carefully read the recipe with an adult. This person can show you how to use any tools you may need and answer any of your questions.

Next, be sure you are wearing the right clothes. Wear shirts with short sleeves, and wear an apron to keep your clothes clean. If you have long hair, keep it away from the food by tying it back.

Once you are dressed for cooking, gather together all the food and tools you will need, such as pans and measuring spoons and cups.

Be sure you have potholders to handle pans that are hot. And don't forget to have paper towels or a damp cloth near you so that you can clean up right away any food that spills. Food on the floor can make you slip and fall.

Once you have everything you need to start, always wash your hands with soap and water before you touch the food.

Finally, after you are done cooking, put away all the food you did not use in your recipe, and wash and put away any dishes or pots you used.

Following these rules before and after you cook will keep you safe and help make you a good cook.

Turn the page.

Answer the questions below.

1 **What do you do before you get out the food you need for the recipe?**

- ○ Wash your hands.
- ○ Put on an apron.
- ○ Wash the pots you used.
- ○ Find some potholders.

2 **When should you wash your hands?**

- ○ before you get the tools you will need
- ○ before you tie your hair back
- ○ before you begin to handle the food
- ○ before you clean up any spills

3 **What do you do after you finish cooking?**

- ○ Wash your hands again.
- ○ Read the recipe carefully.
- ○ Make sure you have potholders.
- ○ Clean up the kitchen.

4 **What is the first thing you do after you choose your recipe and why?**

_____

_____

_____

_____

_____

5 **What is the goal of most of these cooking rules?**

_____

_____

_____

_____

_____

Read the selection. Then answer the questions that follow.

Model T

Many people think that Henry Ford made the first car, but people were driving cars before Henry Ford made the Model T. People also used horses and wagons or rode on trains. Cars cost a lot of money.

What Henry Ford did was to make a car that almost anyone could buy. He did this by changing the way cars were made. His factory had a moving belt that carried car parts past workers as they stood in a line. Each worker did just one part of the job. Building cars this way saved money.

In 1925 a Model T cost only $260. It was not fancy and came in black only, but people loved it. They started to trade their horses for Model Ts. Our life has never been the same.

Turn the page.

Answer the questions below.

1 **What conclusion can you draw about Henry Ford?**

○ He was mostly interested in making luxury cars.

○ He was more interested in helping people than in making money.

○ He believed that people would buy more cars if they cost less.

○ He wanted to change people's way of life.

2 **Which sentence from the selection is a statement of opinion?**

○ He did this by changing the way cars were made.

○ In 1925 a Model T cost only $260.

○ The Model T was not fancy and came in black only, but people loved it.

○ People started to trade their horses for Model Ts.

3 **Why do people think Henry Ford made the first car?**

○ because he was making cars before the Model T

○ because the Model T was the first black car

○ because the Model T was the first really popular car

○ because he taught workers how to do part of the job

4 **What is one way life was different before people owned cars?**

_____

_____

_____

_____

_____

_____

_____

_____

_____

_____

_____

_____

Read the selection. Then answer the questions that follow.

Bird Songs

You probably hear birds singing every day, but did you ever wonder how and why they sing?

Birds sing by using something called a syrinx. It is a tube with two sides, deep inside the bird's chest, which allows the bird to sing two notes at the same time, or to breathe through one side and sing with the other. Birds can make trilling sounds and chuckling sounds, as well as many, many more.

As you probably know, some birds can even talk. Parrots can talk because they have thick tongues, like humans, to shape the sounds they make with the syrinx. Smaller birds, like budgies, use their syrinx in special ways to make human sounds.

Not all birds sing, but all birds make particular sounds to communicate with other birds. We call these sounds bird calls. Birds call to announce danger and may have several calls to describe different kinds of danger. They call to mark the borders of the area where they live. To guard their surroundings, birds call to tell other birds to stay away.

Male birds use their call hoping that a female bird will like it so they can begin a family. The male bird's call is also intended to scare away other male birds that are looking for a female. Young birds make distress calls, which bring adult birds to their aid. Young birds also make feeding calls, which say they're very hungry and need food right now!

Now when you hear a bird singing or calling, you will know that it is sending an important message.

Turn the page.

© Pearson Education 3

Answer the questions below.

1 **Which of the following best describes this selection?**

   ◯ It contains all statements of fact.

   ◯ It contains all statements of opinion.

   ◯ It contains mostly statements of fact.

   ◯ It contains mostly statements of opinion.

2 **After reading this selection, what can you conclude about bird calls?**

   ◯ Birds call only when they cannot sing.

   ◯ Bird calls are more beautiful than bird songs.

   ◯ Calls are the way birds talk to each other.

   ◯ Calls are made mostly to tell other birds what to do.

3 **What can you conclude about the difference between bird songs and bird calls?**

   ◯ Bird calls are more varied than bird songs.

   ◯ All birds can both sing and call.

   ◯ All birds sing, but only some birds call.

   ◯ All birds call, but only some birds sing.

4 **What can you conclude about birds that make feeding calls?**

   ◯ They are warning other birds to stay away.

   ◯ They are very young birds.

   ◯ They have found food for their babies.

   ◯ They are flying around looking for food.

5 **What kind of danger do you think a bird call might tell about?**

_____

_____

_____

_____

_____

_____

_____

Read the selection. Then answer the questions that follow.

Amazing Snakes

When most people hear the word *snake*, they think of something slimy and

dangerous. In fact, snakes are not slimy and are only dangerous if you scare them

or bother them. Some people even want snakes around their homes or barns because

snakes eat rats, mice, and insects.

Snakes are amazing because they do not have legs, ears, or eyelids, yet they can

do all the things other animals can do, like hunt and protect themselves.

All snakes have clear scales over their eyes instead of eyelids, which is why they

always look wide-awake.

Snakes use their forked tongues to smell, so when a snake is hungry, it tastes the

ground or air with its tongue, then brings the tongue to a special sense organ in its

mouth that tells the snake what it has smelled. If it smells something it wants to eat,

it follows the scent.

Snakes protect themselves in different ways. Some snakes hiss, and some shake

the rattles on their tails as a warning, while others play dead, hoping that the ground

will hide them. Some rely on looking like the ground or woods where they live.

All snakes are cold-blooded. This means that their body temperature depends on

the temperature outside their bodies. This is why snakes look for shady, cool spots

when it is hot out and sunny rocks to lie on when it's cold.

Some people say that snakes make the best pets because they only eat once a

week and do not need to go for a walk. Don't let them fool you. It is not that easy

to give a good home to the amazing snake.

Turn the page.

- -

Answer the questions below.

1 What conclusion can you draw about snakes based on the selection?

- ○ Snakes are not dangerous.
- ○ Snakes may be dangerous if you surprise them.
- ○ Snakes are always dangerous.
- ○ Snakes are only dangerous if the weather is warm.

2 Why do you think the author says that snakes are amazing?

- ○ because they are so different from us
- ○ because they are able to protect themselves
- ○ because they are eat mice
- ○ because they are not slimy

3 Which of the following is a statement of fact?

- ○ Most people should not be afraid when they hear the word *snake*.
- ○ Snakes are amazing because they do not have legs, ears, or eyelids.
- ○ All snakes have clear scales over their eyes instead of eyelids.
- ○ It is not that easy to give a good home to the amazing snake.

4 Why would it not do any good to yell at a snake to scare it away?

_____

_____

_____

_____

_____

5 In what two ways are snakes useful to humans?

_____

_____

_____

_____

_____

Read the selection. Then answer the questions that follow.

Friend of Nature

Some people say that Rachel Carson was a hero. Others say she was foolish. No matter what people say about her, she will always be remembered.

Rachel Carson wrote books about the world of nature in which we live. Her final book, *Silent Spring,* warned about the dangers of poisons used to kill insects. These poisons are called pesticides. She told about how they killed birds as well as insects. She told about dangers to fish and other creatures. She called for changes in the use of these poisons. Many people who produced and used the pesticides fought against making those changes. For Rachel Carson, it was important to keep the world safe for all living things. She wrote to tell people how she felt.

People will always thank this brave woman. She taught us that keeping all living things safe is every person's job.

© Pearson Education 3

Turn the page.

Answer the questions below.

1 What was the author's main purpose in writing this selection?

    ○ to persuade the reader to admire Rachel Carson

    ○ to give some facts about Rachel Carson's life

    ○ to warn against the use of pesticides

    ○ to describe Rachel Carson's feelings

2 Why did the author describe Rachel Carson as brave?

    ○ to give more information about her

    ○ to make the reader curious

    ○ to tell how everyone felt about her

    ○ to show that she was not always popular

3 Which of the following is a statement of fact about Rachel Carson?

    ○ Rachel Carson was a hero.

    ○ Rachel Carson was foolish.

    ○ Rachel Carson wrote *Silent Spring*.

    ○ Rachel Carson will always be remembered.

4 Why did the author say that some people thought Rachel Carson was foolish?

_____

_____

_____

_____

_____

_____

_____

_____

_____

_____

_____

Read the selection. Then answer the questions that follow.

Wolves of the Sea

The orca, or killer whale, is the biggest animal in the dolphin family. Like other dolphins, it has a blowhole on the top of its head so it can breathe air. Killer whales live and hunt together in families called pods, much the way wolves in a pack live and hunt together. This is why killer whales are sometimes called wolves of the sea.

Each pod makes its own special sound so that the whales that live in the same pod can recognize their family. The clicks and whistles killer whales make also help them communicate when they're hunting.

Killer whales are black with white patches. They can grow to be as long as twenty-eight feet and weigh twelve thousand pounds or more. They have teeth in both jaws, each tooth being about three inches long and one inch in diameter. Killer whales can swim as fast as thirty miles per hour when they are chasing their prey. They will eat almost any sea animal, including turtles, seals, other whales, and even birds.

These beautiful black-and-white whales live all over the world. People are sometimes lucky enough to see the giants when they leap out of the water. Killer whales also like to slap their tails on top of the water, but no one knows why they do these things.

Because they are so beautiful and easy to train, they are often used in movies and marine animal shows, working closely with people.

Whether you see a killer whale in a movie, in a park, or in the ocean, it will be a sight you will never forget.

Turn the page.

Answer the questions below.

1 **Why did the author write this selection?**

   ◯ to make you want to protect killer whales

   ◯ to inform you about killer whales

   ◯ to describe how killer whales hunt

   ◯ to warn you about a dangerous animal

2 **Why did the author use the words *clicks* and *whistles* to describe the sounds the whales make?**

   ◯ because other whales use clicks and whistles

   ◯ to show that whales sound like humans

   ◯ to let you know that the author has heard whales

   ◯ to help you understand how whales sound

3 **Why did the author probably use the term *killer whales* more often than *orcas?***

   ◯ *Killer whales* is the more scientific term.

   ◯ *Killer whales* sounds more exciting than *orcas*.

   ◯ The term *killer whales* is shorter than the term *orcas*.

   ◯ There are more *killer whales* than there are *orcas*.

4 **What is the author's purpose for including the third paragraph?**

   ◯ to express feelings about the way orcas hunt their prey

   ◯ to inform you about how orcas talk to each other

   ◯ to help you enjoy orcas if you see them

   ◯ to inform you about the size and speed of the orca

5 **Write two statements of fact from this selection.**

_____

_____

_____

_____

_____

_____

Read the selection. Then answer the questions that follow.

The White House

Next to the flag, the White House is the most famous symbol of our government.

When George Washington was President in 1790, he chose the site for this special home for Presidents and oversaw its construction beginning in 1792. The White House was finished eight years later, but he never lived in it because there was a new President. John Adams moved into the house in 1800, and since then every President has lived there.

The White House has six floors (two of them basements), 132 rooms, thirty-two bathrooms, three elevators, and seven staircases. Of the six floors, two are for the President and his family, so visitors cannot go there. But visitors can see the two public floors, and about six thousand people visit them every day.

The White House does not look the same today as it did when it was first built. Wings and floors were added as Presidents needed more room for leaders of other countries who visited, and for storage. Also, because the White House is the President's private home, every President can change the way the rooms look to make his home special for him. But the outside walls of the White House are the same as when it was first built. The stone walls are painted white, and it takes 570 gallons of paint to cover them. The President's house was first officially named the White House in 1901, when Theodore Roosevelt lived there.

You should try to visit the White House, if not in person, then in books. You'll be glad you did.

Turn the page.

Answer the questions below.

1 **Why did the author write this selection?**

   ◯ to tell the reader how Presidents live

   ◯ to express patriotic feelings about the White House

   ◯ to explain how the White House was built

   ◯ to make the reader want to visit the White House

2 **Why did the author tell you the number of rooms and floors in the White House?**

   ◯ to help you understand how big it is

   ◯ to show you how hard it is to get around inside

   ◯ to let you know that not all the rooms are open to visitors

   ◯ to tell you about the history of the building

3 **Which of the following is a statement of opinion?**

   ◯ Next to the flag, the White House is the most famous symbol of our government.

   ◯ John Adams moved into the house in 1800.

   ◯ The White House does not look the same today as it did when it was first built.

   ◯ The President's house was first officially named the White House in 1901.

4 **Why did the author tell you some of the history of the White House?**

_____

_____

_____

_____

_____

5 **Why did the author call the White House a symbol of our government?**

_____

_____

_____

_____

_____

Read the selection. Then answer the questions that follow.

An Orange a Day

For years people have been saying that we should eat fruits and vegetables every day. Why are fruits and vegetables so important?

First of all, fruits and vegetables have vitamin C. Vitamin C is important to help your body fight germs so that you stay healthy. Vitamin C helps heal cuts on your body. It also keeps your gums healthy. Vitamin C helps once you get sick too. Drinking orange juice when you have a cold may help you feel better faster.

Our bodies do not make vitamin C, so we have to get it by eating fruits, such as oranges, and vegetables, such as green and red peppers. To get the most vitamin C from fruits and vegetables, you should eat them soon after you bring them home. Letting fruits get too old kills the vitamins in them.

They say an apple a day keeps the doctor away. Maybe you should eat an orange a day too.

Turn the page.

Answer the questions below.

1 What is this selection about?
- ○ eating enough fruits and vegetables
- ○ getting enough vitamin C
- ○ drinking enough orange juice
- ○ not getting sick

2 What is the most important idea in this selection?
- ○ Our bodies do not make vitamin C.
- ○ Eating makes people healthy.
- ○ Fruits and vegetables should be fresh.
- ○ Vitamin C helps keep us healthy.

3 Which of the following is a detail that tells us more about the main idea?
- ○ Why are fruits and vegetables so important?
- ○ An apple a day keeps the doctor away.
- ○ Fruits and vegetables have vitamin C.
- ○ Older fruit is better for you than fresh fruit.

4 Why would your dentist want you to get plenty of vitamin C?

_____

_____

_____

_____

_____

_____

_____

_____

_____

_____

Read the selection. Then answer the questions that follow.

Strong Mind, Strong Body

Exercising keeps your body strong and your mind sharp. When you run around on the playground or play tag with your friends, not only are you having fun, but you are also improving your body and mind.

Exercise helps your heart stay strong by making it beat faster, and a strong heart will do a better job of getting oxygen to all parts of your body. To make your heart beat faster, try swimming or jumping rope or doing almost anything that works up a sweat. You do not need to buy anything special.

Exercise builds strong muscles and bones. To make your muscles stronger you have to do powerful things, like swinging across the monkey bars at school or lifting heavy things. These exercises will also help build strong bones.

Exercise helps you bend and stretch your body comfortably, which is important when you want to move your arms and legs without hurting them. If you cannot touch your toes, you need to exercise. Try dancing or tumbling to help your body stretch easily.

Exercise makes you feel good about yourself. When you can run and jump, you feel strong and proud of yourself. Your body also releases special chemicals called endorphins that actually make you feel happy.

Exercise helps your brain too. Some people think that exercising helps the blood (and oxygen) flow to your brain so you can think better and pay attention longer.

No matter what kind of exercise you do, it is important that you get moving every day to be healthy and happy.

Turn the page.

Answer the questions below.

1 **What is this selection about?**
- ○ muscles
- ○ exercise
- ○ your brain
- ○ feeling good

2 **What is the main idea of this selection?**
- ○ Playing games is better than doing other exercises.
- ○ Stretching is important in exercising.
- ○ Exercise makes you smarter.
- ○ Exercise keeps your mind and body healthy.

3 **Which detail does not support the idea that exercise is good for you?**
- ○ Exercise helps your heart stay strong.
- ○ Exercise builds strong muscles and bones.
- ○ When you can run and jump you feel strong and proud.
- ○ You do not need to buy anything special to exercise.

4 **What is the main idea of paragraph five?**
- ○ Running and jumping make you strong.
- ○ People are happy when they run and jump.
- ○ Being healthy gives you a good feeling about yourself.
- ○ Endorphins are chemicals that make you feel happy.

5 **Why does exercise help you pay attention longer?**

_____

_____

_____

_____

_____

_____

_____

Read the selection. Then answer the questions that follow.

Sweet Dreams

All animals sleep, some standing up and others lying down, and all people need to sleep too. No one really knows why we sleep, but we know it is important that we get enough sleep.

It looks as if nothing is happening when we sleep, but our bodies and brains are actually very busy. Our bodies are busy building new cells that we need to grow, and repairing any damage we have done during the day. Sleep also helps our immune system to fight off the germs that can make us sick. Without sleep, children do not grow, and we may get sick more often. During sleep, our brains are busy putting our ideas in order and then storing them in our memories. Without sleep it is harder to remember things.

We know that sleep is important because people who do not get enough sleep do things more slowly, get upset easily, make mistakes, and even lose their ability to tell what is real from what is fantasy.

We all need sleep, but how much sleep we need changes as we grow up. A newborn baby sleeps from sixteen to twenty hours a day, but as people get older they need less sleep. The average ten-year-old sleeps ten hours a day. Most adults spend about eight hours asleep. Some older people only spend about six hours a day sleeping.

We may not know why we sleep, but we know that we look better and feel better after a good night's sleep because our bodies and our brains are ready for a new day.

Turn the page.

Answer the questions below.

1 **What is this selection about?**
- ○ dreams
- ○ health
- ○ sleep
- ○ memories

2 **What is the main idea of the selection?**
- ○ Sleep is important to stay healthy.
- ○ All animals and people sleep.
- ○ How much we sleep depends on how old we are.
- ○ Nothing happens while we are sleeping.

3 **What is the main idea of paragraph three?**
- ○ People need to know what is make-believe from what is real.
- ○ People who don't get enough sleep have problems.
- ○ People get upset easily if they don't sleep.
- ○ People who make mistakes easily need sleep.

4 **What are two details that support the main idea of the selection?**

_____

_____

_____

_____

_____

5 **Why do babies sleep so much every day?**

_____

_____

_____

_____

_____

Read the selection. Then answer the questions that follow.

The Mouse and the Lion

Mouse wanted to be just like his friend Lion. After Mouse helped Lion escape from a hunter's net, Lion roared so loudly that the trees shook.

Mouse was amazed. He had a small voice but he wanted to roar like Lion.

"If I practice," thought Mouse, "I'll be able to roar."

So he started practicing. Mouse opened his mouth wide, took a deep breath, and squeaked. Disappointed, Mouse tried again, but he could not roar no matter how many times he tried.

"Lion is tall," thought Mouse. "I'll climb a small tree so I can be as tall as Lion. Then I will roar."

Mouse climbed a holly bush, and now he was as tall as Lion, who was nearby watching Mouse.

Mouse opened his mouth wide, took a deep breath, and squeaked. He tried again but he could not roar.

"Mouse, you should do the special thing that only a mouse can do," said Lion.

Mouse hurried home to practice squeaking.

Turn the page.

Answer the questions below.

1 **What did Mouse learn in this story?**

◯ It is better to do what you know how to do than to try something new.

◯ It is better to be a mouse than a lion.

◯ It is better to concentrate on your strengths than on your weaknesses.

◯ Mouse could be as brave as a lion even if he could not roar.

2 **Why did Mouse want to roar?**

◯ because he liked the way Lion sounded

◯ because he wanted to be friends with Lion

◯ because he wanted to frighten hunters away

◯ because he had a small voice that squeaked

3 **Why couldn't Mouse learn to roar?**

◯ because only tall animals can roar

◯ because he stopped practicing

◯ because Mouse was not special

◯ because he was not a lion

4 **Why did Mouse climb a holly tree?**

_____

_____

_____

_____

_____

_____

_____

_____

_____

Read the selection. Then answer the questions that follow.

Spike's Blue Ribbon

Spike wanted a blue ribbon. All of his friends had at least one ribbon, and they laughed at Spike and told him he would never win a ribbon because his legs were too short and one of his ears would not stand up straight.

Spike was a busy dog, so he did not think about ribbons often. He had to take care of Emma, and that took up all of his time and energy. Every day he had to take Emma for a walk and then let her throw a ball so he could catch it and give it back to her. Emma liked this game, so Spike and Emma did this until Emma got tired. After supper Spike had to sit next to Emma while she did her homework, and later he had to watch Emma until she fell asleep, so by the time he went to bed, Spike was tired.

One night as Spike was watching Emma sleep, he smelled something he had never smelled before, and it made him anxious. Spike jumped off Emma's bed and began to sniff around, and pretty soon he felt hot and his eyes started to hurt. *Fire,* thought Spike, and he started barking to tell Emma to get out, but Emma's mom and dad heard Spike first. They got Emma and ran outside, with Spike running right behind them. When Spike heard the fire truck, he barked to let them know help was coming.

Later everyone said that Spike was a hero, and Emma told Spike he was the best dog in the world. Finally Spike knew how it felt to win a blue ribbon.

Turn the page.

Answer the questions below.

1 Why did Spike bark to tell Emma to get out?

○ because he wanted to win a blue ribbon

○ because he heard a truck coming to the house

○ because he realized there was a fire in the house

○ because Emma would not wake up

2 What did Spike learn in this story?

○ You do not need a blue ribbon to be a winner.

○ Emma's mom and dad could smell fire.

○ Barking is a good way to talk to people.

○ It is more important to play games than to win ribbons.

3 Why did Emma tell Spike he was the best dog in the world?

○ because he heard the fire truck

○ because he saved the family

○ because he finally won a ribbon

○ because he slept on her bed

4 Why did the other dogs laugh at Spike?

○ because he spent so much time with Emma

○ because he never tried to win a ribbon

○ because he did not want to play with them

○ because he was not a very good-looking dog

5 Why did Spike spend so much time with Emma?

_____

_____

_____

_____

_____

_____

_____

Read the selection. Then answer the questions that follow.

Alfonso's Pet

Alfonso wanted a budgie from Australia. He learned about budgies when his class was studying animals that lived in other countries. Alfonso thought budgies were beautiful birds. Also, because they were small parrots, he hoped he could teach his budgie to talk.

When Alfonso asked his mom if he could get a budgie, she told him that they cost too much money. Alfonso reminded his mom that he had saved his allowance. The next time Alfonso asked his mom for a budgie, she reminded him that taking care of a pet was hard work and had to be done every day. Alfonso promised his mom that he would take care of the bird every day after school. Alfonso's mom told him that a budgie needed a special cage, but Alfonso told his mom that he already had a cage that a friend had given him. Alfonso's mom reminded him that budgies needed special food, but Alfonso showed his mom seeds he had already bought, and even told his mom that he would call his budgie Petey.

Alfonso's mom finally agreed. When Alfonso got Petey home, he put the bird into its cage, fed it, and said "Hello" over and over again, hoping Petey would learn to say it too. Every day Alfonso fed Petey, cleaned his cage, and said "Hello." Petey ate the food, played with his toys, but never said a word. Alfonso's mom did not have to remind him to take care of Petey. Alfonso played with Petey every day and taught him to do tricks, and Petey helped Alfonso do his homework by sitting on Alfonso's desk. Soon Alfonso forgot that Petey did not talk. He liked Petey just as he was, quiet and beautiful.

© Pearson Education 3

Turn the page.

Answer the questions below.

1 Why didn't Alfonso's mom want him to get a budgie?
- ○ She did not like budgies.
- ○ She did not like birds.
- ○ She thought Alfonso did not have time for a pet.
- ○ She thought Alfonso would not take care of it.

2 Why do you think Petey sat on Alfonso's desk when Alfonso did his homework?
- ○ Alfonso's desk was near Petey's cage.
- ○ Petey liked being near Alfonso.
- ○ Petey wanted Alfonso to do his homework.
- ○ Alfonso fed Petey at his desk.

3 What did Alfonso learn in this story?
- ○ He could be happy even if things didn't go the way he hoped.
- ○ Having a pet was not as much fun as he thought it would be.
- ○ It was easy to teach budgies to talk.
- ○ Birds do not make good pets.

4 Why did Alfonso stop trying to teach Petey to talk?

_____

_____

_____

_____

_____

5 Why do you think Alfonso got a cage and seeds before he got Petey?

_____

_____

_____

_____

_____

Read the selection. Then answer the questions that follow.

Ray Charles

Ray Charles was born poor and black in 1930. At the age of seven, he became blind. He did not let any of those things stop him. He became one of the world's best musicians.

Ray Charles learned to play the piano at a school for deaf and blind children. After he left school, he played the piano to earn money. For many years he did not earn much money. Then he moved north, and people started to notice him.

Ray Charles worked with Martin Luther King Jr. to help black people. He grew tired of playing in theaters where white people sat close to the stage and his own people had to sit far away from it. He refused to perform under those conditions, even though he needed the money. He wanted all people to be treated the same.

Ray Charles became famous all over the world as a quiet man who could sing any kind of music. He is gone now, but his music will never die.

Turn the page.

Answer the questions below.

1 Which of the following is a statement of fact?

○ Ray Charles was one of the world's best musicians.

○ At the age of seven, he became blind.

○ Ray Charles became famous all over the world.

○ His music will never die.

2 Which of the following best describes this selection?

○ It is all statements of fact.

○ It is all statements of opinion.

○ It contains statements of both fact and opinion.

○ It is not a true account.

3 What is the main idea of this selection?

○ Ray Charles went to a school for deaf and blind children.

○ Ray Charles went all over the world playing his music.

○ Ray Charles was a great musician and a great man.

○ Ray Charles worked with Martin Luther King Jr.

4 Write another statement of fact from this selection.

_____

_____

_____

_____

_____

_____

_____

_____

_____

_____

Read the selection. Then answer the questions that follow.

Morse Code

What if someone said they would send you a message but all you heard was four short taps, a pause, then two short taps? Would you understand the message? If you knew Morse code, you would have heard the letters *HI*.

Samuel Morse invented the Morse code in the 1830s as part of his system for sending messages over wires. His code used a combination of short taps, or dots, and long taps, or dashes, to stand for each letter of the alphabet. By combining dots and dashes, people could send messages across country much faster than they could by Pony Express or carrier pigeon. The first message was sent from Washington, D.C., to Baltimore, Maryland, in 1844, but later, Morse code was used to send messages worldwide.

The most famous three letters in Morse code are probably dot-dot-dot-dash-dash-dash-dot-dot-dot, which stand for SOS. This was a signal sent by someone who needed help. SOS saved thousands of lives at sea. Ships at sea sent the code over a wireless radio or by switching a light on and off. If the light was on for a short time, it meant a dot, and if it lasted a little longer, it was a dash.

Today, with new and better ways to stay in touch on both sea and land, Morse code is no longer used, but SOS still means a cry for help.

The next time you want to send your friend a message, find a list of Morse codes for the alphabet and try tapping it out. You can be pretty sure that no one else will know what you're saying.

Turn the page.

Answer the questions below.

1 Which of the following best describes this selection?

- ○ It is mostly statements of opinion.
- ○ It is mostly statements of fact.
- ○ It is all statements of opinion.
- ○ It is all statements of fact.

2 Which of the following is a statement of fact?

- ○ People do not use Morse code any longer.
- ○ People all over the world know Morse code.
- ○ The most famous letters of the alphabet are SOS.
- ○ Samuel Morse invented a code for sending messages.

3 How do you know that the following sentence is a statement of opinion?
The most famous letters in Morse code are probably SOS.

- ○ The author did not say where the information came from.
- ○ The word *most* is a clue word that the sentence is an opinion.
- ○ There are many ways to prove which letters are the most famous.
- ○ The letters are not really very famous.

4 What is this selection all about?

- ○ the best way to send secret messages to your friends
- ○ the new way Samuel Morse invented to send messages
- ○ how the code SOS saved thousands of lives at sea
- ○ the way Morse code changed the lives of people worldwide

5 What would be a good way to check the facts in this selection?

_____

_____

_____

_____

_____

_____

Read the selection. Then answer the questions that follow.

Money

Money is a part of life. When you go to the store to buy a pencil, for example, you give someone some money and you get your pencil. Money is part of what is called an exchange system.

People need an exchange system, but they do not always use money. In the system of barter, items themselves are exchanged. For example, you might trade a dozen eggs for a dozen pencils or a cow for a rug. Of course, in bartering it is difficult to know if the trade is fair, and trading like this can be a problem. If you are bartering with eggs, salt, or blankets, the eggs could break on the way to the market, the salt could dissolve if it rained, and the blanket would be heavy to carry.

When people began traveling long distances to trade, they wanted something that was easy to carry and hard to damage. They began to use metals such as copper, silver, and gold because they thought the metals were valuable. When a piece of metal was stamped with an image or words, it became flat and round, much like the coins we use today.

Some people used square pieces of brightly colored leather as money, and we think this was the first kind of paper money. Today we print all our bills on special paper, which is strong and easy to carry.

Money continues to change as people's demands change. With the use of computers to buy and sell things, we can now exchange money over wires.

No matter how much the shape of money changes, an exchange system will always be a part of life.

Turn the page.

- -

Answer the questions below.

1 **Which of the following is a statement of opinion?**

○ In the barter system, items themselves are exchanged.

○ People began to use metals in exchange for items.

○ Trading using the barter system can be a problem.

○ Some people used squares of leather as money.

2 **Which of the following best describes this selection?**

○ It contains mostly statements of fact.

○ It contains mostly statements of opinion.

○ It contains all statements of fact.

○ It contains all statements of opinion.

3 **What is the main idea of this selection?**

○ Money consists of metal coins and paper bills.

○ Money is part of what is called an exchange system.

○ What people use for money has changed over the years.

○ Traveling long distances forced people to stop bartering.

4 **How do you know that the following sentence is a statement of opinion?**

"Money is a part of life."

_____

_____

_____

_____

_____

5 **Write one statement of fact about money.**

_____

_____

_____

_____

Read the selection. Then answer the questions that follow.

The Lunch Room

Tyrone watched his friend Jeff push the boy who was in front of him in the lunch line. The small boy was trying hard not to cry. Tyrone wanted to help the boy, but Jeff was popular and Tyrone did not want Jeff to be mad at him.

The next day at lunch Tyrone watched as Jeff pushed the boy's lunch tray off the table, spilling his cake and milk. Tyrone did not know what to do. If he helped the boy, Jeff would be mad at him. If he did not help the boy, he would be mad at himself.

Tyrone talked to his mom and dad about Jeff.

"Sometimes it's not easy to do the right thing," Tyrone's mom said.

The next day when Jeff began to make fun of the boy, Tyrone took a deep breath and told Jeff to stop. When the boy smiled at him, Tyrone knew he had done the right thing. It felt good.

Turn the page.

Answer the questions below.

1 **What did Tyrone learn in this story?**

  ⭕ His friend Jeff was doing good things after all.

  ⭕ His mom and dad gave him good advice.

  ⭕ Helping someone is the right thing to do.

  ⭕ You should think carefully before you do anything.

2 **Which of these was not important to the plot of the story?**

  ⭕ Tyrone watched his friend Jeff push a boy.

  ⭕ The boy had cake and milk on his lunch tray.

  ⭕ Tyrone did not want Jeff to be mad at him.

  ⭕ Tyrone talked to his mom and dad about Jeff.

3 **Why did Tyrone talk to his parents?**

  ⭕ because they always told him what to do

  ⭕ because he did not want Jeff to be mad

  ⭕ because Jeff was going to make fun of him

  ⭕ because he was confused about what to do

4 **Why didn't Tyrone help the boy at first?**

_____

_____

_____

_____

_____

_____

_____

_____

_____

_____

_____

Read the selection. Then answer the questions that follow.

Tanya's New Friend

Mr. Sripathi was born in India and had come to this country only six months ago with his wife and two sons. They all learned English quickly, and, although they thought about India sometimes, they were happy to be here.

One day Mr. Sripathi and his family came to Tanya's house for dinner. Pramit Sripathi was Tanya's age, so Tanya's dad asked her to welcome Pramit to their home. Tanya told him that she was sorry all her video games were old. She asked him if he would like to play some other games. While Tanya got out some board games, Pramit looked around Tanya's room and thought that his whole village did not have as many books, toys, or clothes as this one person had.

At dinner Tanya complained that they were having chicken again. Mr. Sripathi told Tanya's dad that in India sometimes all they had to eat was rice, but now they had fresh vegetables every day. He said that many new friends had helped them get used furniture and clothes for his home and family. But mostly he was thankful that Pramit had books and could go to school.

Tanya had never seen a person so happy about vegetables. She thought about her warm bed, her toys, and all her clothes. Her face got red when she thought how she had complained about her toys and the food.

"Dad, since you made this great meal, I'll clean up the kitchen," Tanya said as she got up to clear the table.

© Pearson Education 3

Turn the page.

Answer the questions below.

1 **What did Tanya learn in this story?**
- ◯ She had a new friend.
- ◯ Her dad was a good cook.
- ◯ She was luckier than she thought.
- ◯ Her video games were not so old after all.

2 **Which of these was most important to the plot of this story?**
- ◯ Pramit Sripathi came over for dinner.
- ◯ They were having chicken for dinner.
- ◯ Tanya got out some board games.
- ◯ The Sripathis had two sons.

3 **Why did Tanya offer to clean up the kitchen at the end?**
- ◯ She liked washing and drying the dishes.
- ◯ Her father had asked her to help him.
- ◯ She was happy that dinner was over.
- ◯ She was ashamed of the way she had acted.

4 **Why did Tanya apologize for her video games?**
- ◯ She wanted Pramit to play a board game.
- ◯ She thought everyone else had newer ones.
- ◯ She wanted Pramit to tell her about his life in India.
- ◯ She did not know what games Pramit had.

5 **Why did Mr. Sripathi tell about their life in India?**

_____

_____

_____

_____

_____

_____

_____

Read the selection. Then answer the questions that follow.

Celebrating Earth Day

Marguerite's class was studying ways of saving Earth's resources. One way was to save trees by using paper over again instead of throwing it away. A boy in Marguerite's class said that his sister made puppets out of small paper bags, and a girl said that they used comics to wrap gifts instead of buying wrapping paper. Marguerite's teacher told the class that for homework they should think of an idea for how to use paper over again.

When Marguerite got home she told her mom about her own idea. "I will make cards for birthdays and holidays using old magazines, paper bags, and the envelopes that letters came in," she said.

Marguerite gathered some paper bags her mom had saved, some old magazines and white envelopes from the recycling bin, glue, scissors, a ruler, and colored markers. Marguerite's mom gave her some pieces of ribbon and old wrapping paper.

Marguerite looked for pictures of beaches because she loved the ocean. Next she cut the paper bags into different-sized pieces and then folded them in half. She glued a picture of a beach on one piece of brown paper, then cut out some cloud shapes from the white paper and glued them on. Then she glued the ribbon around the picture. The front of the card looked great, and it was all made with things that would have been thrown away.

Marguerite was eager to show her card to her teacher and her friends. She decided that she would make more cards, but her first card would be to celebrate Earth Day.

Turn the page.

Answer the questions below.

1   What did Marguerite learn in this story?
   ○ It is easier to buy cards than to make them.
   ○ She wants to show her card to her teacher.
   ○ Saving the Earth's resources can be fun.
   ○ She does not have to wrap presents.

2   Which of these was important to the plot of this story?
   ○ Marguerite's teacher assigned homework.
   ○ Marguerite used a ruler and some glue to make her cards.
   ○ One student used comics to wrap gifts.
   ○ Marguerite glued ribbon around the pictures.

3   What happened after Marguerite told her mom her idea?
   ○ Her mom told her it was a good idea.
   ○ Marguerite hurried home from school.
   ○ Marguerite found ribbon and old wrapping paper.
   ○ Her mom helped her find things to use for the cards.

4   Why did Marguerite want her first card to celebrate Earth Day?

_____

_____

_____

_____

5   Is it important to the plot that Marguerite used a picture of a beach on her card? Explain your answer.

_____

_____

_____

_____

Read the selection. Then answer the questions that follow.

Tamales

Tamales are one of the best foods ever made. I had my first one in Mexico. People in Mexico eat them all the time. They eat tamales on the street like fast food. They eat them at holiday time. They eat them at dinner with the family. People were making and eating tamales in Mexico before Columbus came to America.

Tamales look like pancakes rolled up with filling inside. They can be filled with almost anything. Cheese, fish, and meat are all good fillings. After tamales are made and filled, they are put inside a corn skin. Then they can be roasted in a fire, steamed, or baked. They taste good hot or cold.

Once found mostly in Mexico, tamales are now eaten by people all over the world.

Turn the page.

Answer the questions below.

1 Where will you find the main idea of this selection?

○ in the first sentence of the first paragraph

○ in the second sentence of the second paragraph

○ in the first sentence of the second paragraph

○ in the last sentence of the selection

2 Which of the following statements is not true of most or all tamales?

○ After tamales are filled, they are put inside a corn skin.

○ I had my first one in Mexico.

○ Tamales can be filled with almost anything.

○ They can be eaten hot or cold.

3 What can you say about most or all tamales?

○ People do not eat them cold.

○ Most people like them.

○ They are always filled with cheese.

○ They are never baked in an oven.

4 Why do you think people like tamales so much?

_____

_____

_____

_____

_____

_____

_____

_____

_____

_____

Read the selection. Then answer the questions that follow.

Lighthouses

When people sail out from the coast during the day, they can use landmarks such as hills or rock formations to help them find their way back to where they started. At night these landmarks are harder to see, so in their place people once built fires.

In fact, the first lighthouses were towers with a fire on top. Fire from the first lighthouse we know about could be seen from thirty miles away. That lighthouse, 450 feet high, was built about 280 B.C. and was considered one of the seven wonders of the world. Most lighthouses were built either to warn sailors to stay away from dangerous rocks or shallow water, or to guide them into harbors.

Lighthouses can be tall or short, square or round, depending on where the lighthouse is. They can be made of stone, wood, brick, or cast iron.

Each lighthouse in this country has a special pattern painted on it so that sailors can tell them apart. Some lighthouses have diamond shapes and others look like a checkerboard. This way the lighthouse serves as a landmark during the day as well as at night.

The source of light in the lighthouse is called a lamp, and the place the light shines out of is called the lantern room. Early lighthouses used wood and coal fires and, later, candles and oil lanterns were used for light. Today most of the lamps are electric. The Statue of Liberty was the first lighthouse in this country to use electricity. It served as a lighthouse for its first fifteen years.

Most lighthouses are no longer in use, but they are kept in good condition so that we can visit them and see our history.

Turn the page.

Answer the questions below.

1 Which of the following statements can you make about all lighthouses?

○ They are tall and painted with designs.

○ They were built to help people find their way.

○ They cannot be seen during the day.

○ The Statue of Liberty was a lighthouse.

2 What is the main idea of this selection?

○ Lighthouses have to be near the sea.

○ Different kinds of lighthouses have different kinds of lamps.

○ People do not need lighthouses anymore.

○ Lighthouses are historic places.

3 Which of the following is true about lighthouses in general?

○ Only tall lighthouses guided people at night.

○ A lighthouse was one of the seven wonders of the world.

○ They have square shapes painted on them.

○ Only a few are still being used.

4 Which sentence from the selection is not a general statement?

○ Fire from the first lighthouse could be seen from thirty miles away.

○ The source of light in the lighthouse is called a lamp.

○ Today most of the lamps are electric.

○ Each lighthouse has a special pattern painted on it.

5 Why do people visit lighthouses today?

_____

_____

_____

_____

_____

_____

_____

_____

Read the selection. Then answer the questions that follow.

Adventurer and Hero

What would you call a person who became a doctor, went to Africa to help people, started her own company, and became the first black woman in space? You would call her Dr. Mae Jemison.

During medical school, this amazing woman traveled the world helping sick people. When she became a doctor, she joined the Peace Corps and continued to help sick people in West Africa. Back in this country, she worked as a doctor but also applied to the astronaut training program. At first she did not get in, but she applied again, and this time she was accepted, one of sixteen people accepted from over two thousand who applied. One year later she was an astronaut, and four years after that she was floating in a space lab high over Earth.

After Dr. Jemison decided to stay on Earth, she started the Jemison Group. Her company finds ways to use advanced technology to help people. Helping boys and girls learn about science is also important to Dr. Jemison, so she started a program called The Earth We Share. It is a camp where students ages twelve to sixteen from around the world try to solve problems we all share. One year the campers were asked, "How many people can the Earth hold?" They have four weeks to find the answer. Dr. Jemison's first book was an autobiography written for teenagers.

As busy as Dr. Jemison is, she still finds time to read, cook, dance, garden, play volleyball, and watch movies.

Dr. Jemison has worked hard all her life to do so much, but she is a hero because she never gets tired of helping people.

Turn the page.

Answer the questions below.

1 **Which of the following best describes Dr. Mae Jemison?**

○ She started a program to help children.

○ She never gets tired of helping people.

○ She is never tired or bored.

○ She was accepted into astronaut training.

2 **What is the most important idea in this selection?**

○ Dr. Jemison wanted to help people by going into space.

○ We should have more woman astronauts.

○ Dr. Jemison is a doctor who works to help others.

○ People in Africa are thankful for Dr. Jemison.

3 **Which of the following statements is true of the astronaut training?**

○ Most people who apply are doctors or engineers.

○ No one is accepted the first time they apply.

○ The people who apply want to help others.

○ Few people are accepted into the program.

4 **How would you describe a hero?**

_____

_____

_____

_____

5 **What did you learn from the selection about what Dr. Mae Jemison is like?**

_____

_____

_____

_____